Level 1

BENCHMARK SERIES

Microsoft® Word

Review and Assessment

Nita Rutkosky

Audrey Roggenkamp
Pierce College Puyallup
Puyallup, Washington

Ian Rutkosky
Pierce College Puyallup
Puyallup, Washington

A DIVISION OF KENDALL HUNT

Minneapolis

Cover Photo Credit: © lowball-jack/GettyImages

ISBN 978-0-76388-717-9 (print)

7900 Xerxes Avenue S STE 310
Minneapolis, MN 55431-1118
Email: CustomerService@ParadigmEducation.com
Website: ParadigmEducation.com

Printed in the United States of America

Contents

Microsoft®

Word Level 1

Unit 1

Editing and Formatting Documents

Preparing a Word Document

The online course includes additional review and assessment resources.

Skills Assessment

Assessment 1

Edit a Document on Resume Writing

1. Open Word and then open **WriteResume**.
2. Save the document and name it **1-WriteResume**.
3. Move the insertion point to the end of the document and then type the text shown in Figure 1.1. When typing the text, use the New Line command, Shift + Enter, to end the lines after *Created by Marie Solberg* and *Monday, October 4, 2021*.
4. Make the following changes to the document:
   a. Delete the first occurrence of the word *currently* in the first sentence of the first paragraph.
   b. Select the word *important* in the first sentence in the first paragraph and then type essential.
   c. Type and hard-hitting between the words *concise* and *written* in the second sentence of the second paragraph.
   d. Delete the words *over and over,* (including the comma and the space after the comma) in the third sentence in the second paragraph.
   e. Select and then delete the second sentence of the third paragraph (the sentence that begins *So do not take*).
   f. Move the insertion point to the beginning of the third paragraph and then press the backspace key to join the third paragraph with the second paragraph.
   g. Delete the name *Marie Solberg* and then type your first and last names.
5. Save, print, and then close **1-WriteResume**.

Figure 1.1 Assessment 1

Created by Marie Solberg
Monday, October 4, 2021
Note: Please insert this information between the 2nd and 3rd sections.

Assessment 2

Check the Spelling and Grammar of a Resume Style Document

1. Open **ResumeStyles**.
2. Save the document with the name **1-ResumeStyles**.
3. Complete a spelling and grammar check on the document and correct the errors.
4. Type the sentence Different approaches work for different people. between the first and second sentences in the first paragraph of text below the title *RESUME STYLES*.
5. Move the insertion point to the end of the document (on the blank line following the last paragraph of text), type your first and last names, press Shift + Enter, and then type the current date.
6. Save, print, and then close **1-ResumeStyles**.

Assessment 3

Create a Document Describing Keyboard Shortcuts

1. Press the F1 function key to display the Help task pane.
2. Type keyboard shortcuts in the search text box and then press the Enter key.
3. In the Help task pane, click the Keyboard shortcuts for Microsoft Word on Windows hyperlink. (If this article is not available, choose a similar article that describes Word keyboard shortcuts.)
4. Read through the information in the Help task pane.
5. Open a new blank single-spaced document.
6. Create a document with the following specifications:
   a. Type Keyboard Shortcuts as the title.
   b. Describe four keyboard shortcuts by providing a brief description of how each shortcut is used.
   c. Click in the title *Keyboard Shortcuts* and then use the Tell Me feature to center the title.
7. Save the document and name it **1-KeyboardShortcuts**.
8. Print and then close **1-KeyboardShortcuts**.

Visual Benchmark

Create a Cover Letter

1. At a new blank document, type the cover letter shown in Figure 1.2, following the directions in red. (A cover letter is a business letter written to accompany a resume. It may be sent electronically or through the mail. When sent through the mail, a cover letter should include the postal address of the writer and the addressee in block paragraph format, as shown in Figure 1.2.)
2. Save the completed letter and name it **1-CoverLtr**.
3. Print and then close the document.

Figure 1.2 Visual Benchmark

(press Enter three times)

4520 South Park Street *(press Shift + Enter)*
Newark, NJ 07122 *(press Shift + Enter)*
Current Date *(press Enter two times)*

Ms. Sylvia Hammond *(press Shift + Enter)*
Sales Director, Eastern Division *(press Shift + Enter)*
Grand Style Products *(press Shift + Enter)*
1205 Sixth Street *(press Shift + Enter)*
Newark, NJ 07102 *(press Enter)*

Dear Ms. Hammond: *(press Enter)*

Thank you for agreeing to meet with me next Wednesday. Based on our initial conversation, I believe that my ability to sell solutions rather than products is a good fit for your needs as you seek to expand your visibility in the region. *(press Enter)*

As noted in the enclosed resume, I have led an underperforming product division to generating 33 percent of total revenue (up from 5 percent) at our location. We now deliver, from a single location, 25 percent of total sales for our 20-site company. Having completed this turnaround over the last 5 years, I'm eager for new challenges that will enable me to use my proven skills in sales, marketing, and program/event planning to contribute to a company's bottom line. *(press Enter)*

I have been thinking about the challenges you described in building your presence at the retail level, and I have some good ideas to share at our meeting. I am excited about the future of Grand Style Products and eager to contribute to the company's growth. *(press Enter)*

Sincerely, *(press Enter two times)*

Student Name *(press Enter)*

Enclosure

Case Study

Part 1

You are the administrative assistant at a mid-sized service-oriented business. Employees frequently use Microsoft Word to create contracts to use with customers. Your boss, Mr. Brewster, wants these saved to a folder named *Contracts* in the Documents folder on your company's shared drive. Mr. Brewster has asked you to create a document for employees with step-by-step instructions for naming and saving contracts. Save your completed document with the name **1-Saving**. Print and then close the document.

Part 2

Mr. Brewster would like to have a document describing basic Word commands and keyboard shortcuts to help employees work more efficiently in Microsoft Word. He has asked you to prepare a document containing the following information:

- A brief explanation of how to use the Go To feature to move the insertion point to a specific page
- Keyboard shortcuts to move the insertion point to the beginning and end of a line and the beginning and end of a document
- Keyboard commands to delete text from the insertion point to the beginning of a word and from the insertion point to the end of a word
- Steps to select a word and a paragraph using the mouse
- A keyboard shortcut to select the entire document

Save the completed document and name it **1-WordCommands**. Print and then close the document.

Part 3

According to Mr. Brewster, the company is considering updating its computers to Microsoft Office 365. He has asked you to go to the Microsoft home page at microsoft.com and then use the Search feature to find information on Office 365 plans for use in business. Determine what applications and services are included and pricing for each plan. When you find the information, type a document that contains information on two different Office 365 plans. Save the document and name it **1-Office365**. Print and then close the document.

Microsoft® Word
Review and Assessment

Formatting Characters and Paragraphs

The online course includes additional review and assessment resources.

Skills Assessment

Assessment 1

Apply Character Formatting to a Lease Agreement Document

1. Open **LeaseAgrmnt** and then save it with the name **2-LeaseAgrmnt**.
2. Press Ctrl + End to move the insertion point to the end of the document, press the Enter key, and then type the text shown in Figure 2.1. Bold, italicize, and underline text as shown.
3. Select the entire document and then change the font to Candara and the font size to 12 points.
4. Select and then bold *THIS LEASE AGREEMENT* in the first paragraph.
5. Select and then italicize *12 o'clock midnight* in the *Term* section.
6. Select the title *LEASE AGREEMENT* and then change the font to 16-point Corbel and the font color to standard dark blue. (The title should remain bold.)
7. Select the heading *Term*, change the font to 14-point Corbel, and then apply small caps formatting. (The heading should remain bold.)
8. Use Format Painter to change the formatting to small caps in 14-point Corbel bold for the remaining headings (*Rent*, *Damage Deposit*, *Use of Premises*, *Condition of Premises*, *Damage to Premises*, and *Inspection of Premises*).
9. Save, print, and then close **2-LeaseAgrmnt**.

Figure 2.1 Assessment 1

Inspection of Premises

Lessor shall have the right to exhibit the Premises and to display a *for rent* sign on the Premises at any time within forty-five days before the expiration of this Lease.

Assessment 2 — Apply Styles, a Style Set, and a Modified Theme to a Hardware Technology Document

1. Open **NetworkHardware** and then save it with the name **2-NetworkHardware**.
2. Apply the Heading 1 style to the title *Network Hardware*.
3. Apply the Heading 2 style to the headings in the document (*Hubs*, *Switches*, *Repeaters*, *Routers*, *Gateways*, *Bridges*, and *Network Interface Cards*).
4. Apply the Lines (Stylish) style set.
5. Apply the Banded theme.
6. Apply the Orange theme colors.
7. Apply the Candara theme fonts.
8. Apply the Open paragraph spacing.
9. Highlight in yellow the second sentence in the *Hubs* section (the sentence that begins with *The hub is usually*).
10. Save, print, and then close **2-NetworkHardware**.

Assessment 3 — Apply Character and Paragraph Formatting to an Employee Privacy Document

1. Open **WorkPrivacy** and then save it with the name **2-WorkPrivacy**.
2. Select the text from the beginning of the first paragraph to the end of the document (including the blank line following the last paragraph) and then make the following changes:
   a. Change the line spacing to 1.5 lines.
   b. Change the spacing after paragraphs to 0 points.
   c. Indent the first line of each paragraph 0.5 inch.
   d. Change the paragraph alignment to justified.
3. Move the insertion point to the end of the document, drag the First Line Indent marker on the horizontal ruler back to 0 inches, and then type the text shown in Figure 2.2. (Create a hanging indent as shown in the figure.)
4. Select the entire document and then change the font to Constantia.
5. Select the title *WORKPLACE PRIVACY* and then apply the following formatting:
   a. Center the title.
   b. Change the font to 14-point Calibri.
   c. Click the Text Effects and Typography button and then click the option in the second column, first row (blue fill and shadow).
6. Use the Format Painter to apply the same formatting to the title *BIBLIOGRAPHY* that you applied to the title *WORKPLACE PRIVACY*.
7. Save, print, and then close **2-WorkPrivacy**.

Figure 2.2 Assessment 3

BIBLIOGRAPHY

Nye, H. G. (2021). *Privacy in the workplace*, 2nd edition (pp. 103-112). Denver, CO: Goodwin Publishing Group.

Visual Benchmark

Create a Report about Active Listening Skills

1. Open **ActiveListen** and then save it with the name **2-ActiveListen**.
2. Apply the following formatting to the document so it appears as shown in Figure 2.3:
   a. Select the document and then change the font to 12-point Cambria and the font color to standard dark blue.
   b. Set the title in 16-point Candara bold and center the title.
   c. Set the headings in 14-point Candara bold.
   d. Change the paragraph spacing after the title and headings to 6 points.
   e. Underline the text as shown in the figure.
   f. Create a hanging indent for the paragraphs as shown in the figure.
3. Save, print, and then close **2-ActiveListen**.

Figure 2.3 Visual Benchmark

ACTIVE LISTENING SKILLS

Listening is a two-way activity. When the audience pays attention, the speaker gains confidence, knowing that his or her message is being received and appreciated. At the same time, alert listeners obtain information, hear an amusing or interesting story, and otherwise benefit from the speaker's presentation.

Become an Active Listener

Active listeners pay attention to the speaker and to what is being said. They are respectful of the speaker and eager to be informed or entertained. In contrast, *passive listeners* "tune out" the presentation and may even display rudeness by not paying attention to the speaker. Here are ways in which you can become an active listener:

Listen with a purpose: Stay focused on what the speaker is saying, and you will gain useful information or hear a suspenseful story narrated well. Try to avoid letting your attention wander.

Be courteous: Consider that the speaker spent time preparing for the presentation and thus deserves your respect.

Take brief notes: If the speaker is providing information, take brief notes on the main ideas. Doing so will help you understand and remember what is being said. If you have questions or would like to hear more about a particular point, ask the speaker for clarification after the presentation.

Practice Active Listening Skills in Conversation

Most people have had the experience of being in a one-way conversation, in which one person does all the talking and the others just listen. In fact, this is not a conversation, which is by definition an exchange of information and ideas. In a true conversation, everyone has a chance to be heard. Do not monopolize conversation. Give the other person or persons an opportunity to talk. Pay attention when others are speaking, and show your interest in what is being said by making eye contact and asking questions. Avoid interrupting, since this shows your disinterest and also suggests that what you have to say is more important.

Case Study

Part 1

You work for the local chamber of commerce and are responsible for assisting the office manager, Teresa Alexander. Ms. Alexander would like to maintain consistency in articles submitted for publication in the monthly chamber newsletter. She wants you to explore various decorative and plain fonts. She would like you to choose two handwriting fonts, two decorative fonts, and two plain fonts and then prepare a document containing an example of each font. Save the document and name it **2-Fonts**. Print and then close the document.

Part 2

Ms. Alexander has asked you to write a short article for the chamber newsletter. In the article, you are to describe an upcoming event at your school or in your community. Effectively use at least two of the fonts you selected in Case Study Part 1. Save the document and name it **2-Article**. Print and then close the document.

Part 3

Ms. Alexander will be posting the newsletter to the chamber's website and would like you to explain how to save a Word document as a web page. Display the Save As dialog box and then determine how to save a document as a filtered web page using the *Save as type* option. Create a Word document with step-by-step instructions. Save the document and name it **2-WebPage**. Print and then close the document. Open **2-Article,** the document you created in Case Study Part 2, and then save the document as a filtered web page.

Microsoft® Word
Review and Assessment

Customizing Paragraphs

The online course includes additional review and assessment resources.

Skills Assessment

Assessment 1

Format and Sort a Computer Ethics and Timeline Document

1. Open **CompTech** and then save it with the name **3-CompTech**.
2. Move the insertion point to the end of the document and then type the text shown in Figure 3.1. (Type the > symbol and press the spacebar for the first item and the symbol will be formatted as an arrow bullet, and the bullet for each remaining item will be inserted automatically.)
3. Select the three paragraphs below the heading *Computer Ethics* and then apply numbered formatting.
4. Select the eleven paragraphs below the heading *Technology Timeline* and then apply bulleted formatting. (Arrow bullets will be applied to the paragraphs.)
5. With the eleven paragraphs still selected, sort the paragraphs in descending order.
6. Type the following paragraph of text between paragraphs 2 and 3 below the heading *Computer Ethics*: Find sources relating to the latest legislation on privacy protection. ***Note: The new paragraph will be the third item in the numbered list.***
7. Apply the Lines (Distinctive) style set. (Click the Design tab to display style sets.)
8. Apply the Slice theme. (Click the Design tab to display the Theme button.)
9. Apply Light Turquoise, Background 2, Lighter 80% paragraph shading (third column, second row in the *Theme Colors* section) to the numbered paragraphs below the heading *COMPUTER ETHICS* and the bulleted paragraphs below the heading *TECHNOLOGY TIMELINE* and the heading *WINDOWS OPERATING SYSTEM VERSIONS*.
10. Save, print, and then close **3-CompTech**.

Figure 3.1 Assessment 1

➢ Windows Vista
➢ Windows 7
➢ Windows 8
➢ Windows 10

Assessment 2 Type Tabbed Text and Apply Formatting to a Computer Software Document

1. Open **ProdSoftware** and then save it with the name **3-ProdSoftware**.
2. Move the insertion point to the end of the document and then set left tabs at the 0.75-inch, 2.75-inch, and 4.5-inch marks on the horizontal ruler. Type the text in Figure 3.2 at the tabs you set. Use the New Line command, Shift + Enter, after typing each line of text in columns (except the last line).
3. Apply the Retrospect theme.
4. Select the productivity software categories in the *Productivity Software* section (from *Word processing* through *Computer-aided design*) and then sort the text alphabetically.
5. With the text still selected, apply bulleted formatting. (Solid circle bullets will be applied to the text.)
6. Select the personal-use software categories in the *Personal-Use Software* section (from *Personal finance software* through *Games and entertainment software*) and then sort the text alphabetically.
7. With the text still selected, apply bulleted formatting.
8. Apply to the heading *Productivity Software* a single-line top border and Olive Green, Text 2, Lighter 80% paragraph shading (fourth column, second row in the *Theme Colors* section).
9. Apply the same single-line top border and olive green shading to the other two headings (*Personal-Use Software* and *Software Training Schedule*).
10. Position the insertion point in the first line of tabbed text and then move the tab symbols on the horizontal ruler as follows:
    a. Move the tab at the 0.75-inch mark to the 1-inch mark.
    b. Move the tab at the 4.5-inch mark to the 4-inch mark.
11. Save, print, and then close **3-ProdSoftware**.

Figure 3.2 Assessment 2

Word	April 20	8:30 to 11:30 a.m.
PowerPoint	April 22	1:00 to 3:30 p.m.
Excel	May 11	8:30 to 11:30 a.m.
Access	May 13	1:00 to 3:30 p.m.

Assessment 3 Type and Format a Table of Contents Document

1. At a new blank document, type the document shown in Figure 3.3 with the following specifications:
    a. Change the font to 11-point Cambria.
    b. Apply bold formatting and center alignment to the title as shown.
    c. Before typing the tabbed text, display the Tabs dialog box. Set a left tab at the 1-inch mark and the 1.5-inch mark and a right tab with period leaders at the 5.5-inch mark.
    d. When typing the text, press the Enter key to end each line of text.
2. Save the document and name it **3-TofC**.
3. Print **3-TofC**.
4. Select the tabbed text and then move the tab symbols on the horizontal ruler as follows. (Because you pressed the Enter key instead of Shift + Enter at the end of each line of text, you need to select all the tabbed text before moving the tabs.)

a. Delete the left tab symbol at the 1.5-inch mark.
b. Set a new left tab at the 0.5-inch mark.
c. Move the right tab at the 5.5-inch mark to the 6-inch mark.

5. Insert single-line borders above and below the title *TABLE OF CONTENTS*.
6. Apply Orange, Accent 2, Lighter 80% paragraph shading (sixth column, second row in the *Theme Colors* section) to the title *TABLE OF CONTENTS*.
7. Save, print, and then close **3-TofC**.

Figure 3.3 Assessment 3

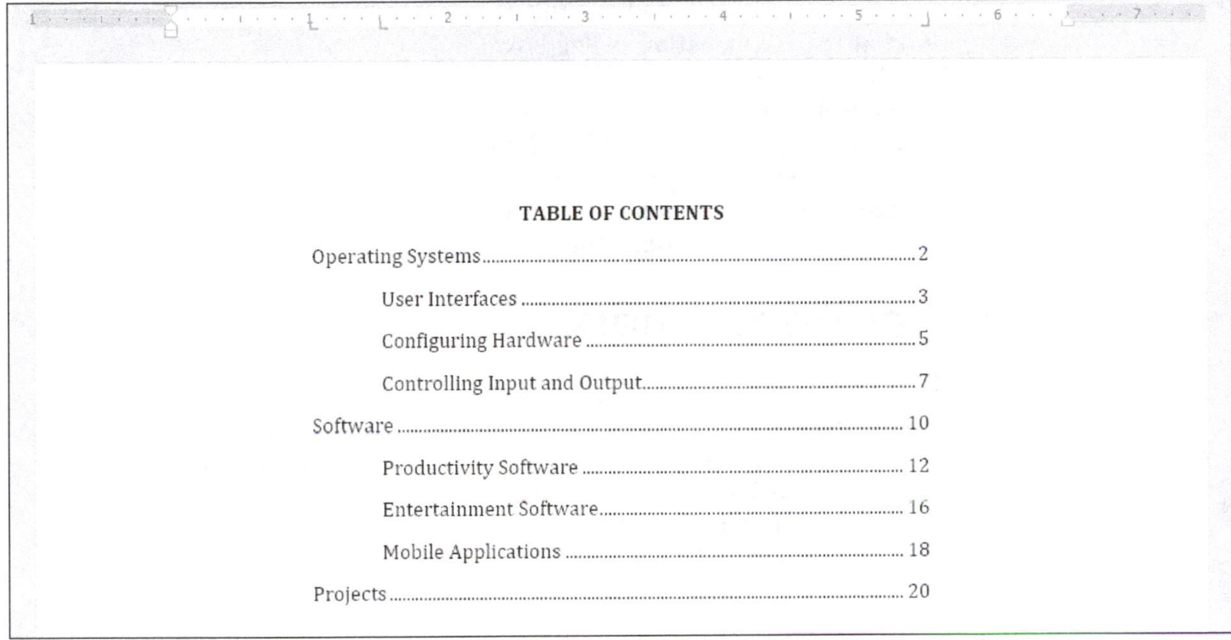

TABLE OF CONTENTS

Operating Systems.......... 2
User Interfaces 3
Configuring Hardware 5
Controlling Input and Output.......... 7
Software 10
Productivity Software 12
Entertainment Software.......... 16
Mobile Applications 18
Projects.......... 20

Assessment 4 — Format a Building Construction Agreement Document

1. Open **ConstructAgrmnt** and then save it with the name **3-ConstructAgrmnt**.
2. Select and then delete the paragraph that begins *SUPERVISION OF WORK*.
3. Move the paragraph that begins *FINANCE AGREEMENT* before the paragraph that begins *START OF CONSTRUCTION*.
4. Open **AgrmntItems**.
5. Display the Clipboard task pane and then clear all the contents, if necessary.
6. Select and then copy the first paragraph.
7. Select and then copy the second paragraph.
8. Select and then copy the third paragraph.
9. Close **AgrmntItems**.
10. With **3-ConstructAgrmnt** open, display the Clipboard task pane.
11. Position the insertion point at the beginning of the *CHANGES AND ALTERATIONS* paragraph and then paste the *SUPERVISION* paragraph and merge the formatting.
12. Position the insertion point at the beginning of the *POSSESSION OF RESIDENCE* paragraph and then paste the *PAY REVIEW* paragraph and merge the formatting.
13. Clear all items from the Clipboard and then close the Clipboard task pane.
14. Save, print, and then close **3-ConstructAgrmnt**.

Assessment 5

Hyphenate Words in a Report

1. In some Word documents, especially documents with left and right margins wider than 1 inch, the right margin may appear quite ragged. If the paragraph alignment is changed to justified alignment, the right margin will appear even, but extra space will be added between words throughout the line. In these situations, hyphenating long words that fall at the ends of text lines provides the document with a more balanced look. Click the Layout tab and then explore the options available in the Hyphenation button drop-down list in the Page Setup group. Figure out how to automatically hyphenate words in a document and how to limit the number of consecutive hyphens using an option at the Hyphenation dialog box.
2. Open **InterfaceApps** and then save it with the name **3-InterfaceApps**.
3. Automatically hyphenate words in the document, limiting the number of consecutive hyphens to two. ***Hint: Display the Hyphenation dialog box by clicking the Hyphenation button in the Page Setup group on the Layout tab and then clicking*** **Hyphenation Options.**
4. Save, print, and then close **3-InterfaceApps**.

Visual Benchmark

Create a Resume

1. Open **Resume** and then save it with the name **3-Resume**.
2. Apply character and paragraph formatting to the resume so it appears as shown in Figure 3.4.
3. Save, print, and then close **3-Resume**.

Figure 3.4 Visual Benchmark

DEVON CHAMBERS

344 North Anderson Road * Oklahoma City, OK 73177 * (404) 555-3228

PROFILE

Business manager with successful track record at entrepreneurial start-up and strong project management skills. Keen ability to motivate and supervise employees, a strong hands-on experience with customer service, marketing, and operations. Highly organized and motivated professional looking to leverage strengths in leadership and organizational skills in a project coordinator role.

PROFESSIONAL EXPERIENCE

Midwest Deli, Oklahoma City, OK..07/19 to present
Assistant Manager

- Coordinated the opening of a new business, which included budgeting start-up costs, establishing relationships with vendors, ordering supplies, purchasing and installing equipment, and marketing the business to the community
- Manage business personnel, which includes recruitment, interviewing, hiring, training, motivating staff, and resolving conflicts
- Manage daily business operations through customer satisfaction, quality control, employee scheduling, process improvement, and product inventory maintenance

Marin Associates, Shawnee, OK...06/17 to 06/19
Projects Coordinator

- Developed and maintained a secure office network and installed and repaired computers
- Provided support for hardware and software issues
- Directed agency projects such as equipment purchases, office reorganization, and building maintenance and repair

Moore Insurance Agency, Shawnee, OK...04/15 to 05/17
Administrative Assistant

- Prepared documents and forms for staff and clients
- Organized and maintained paper and electronic files and scheduled meetings and appointments
- Disseminated information using the telephone, mail services, websites, and email

EDUCATION

Associate of Arts, Business..2019
Oklahoma City Community College

TECHNOLOGY SKILLS

- Proficient in Microsoft Word, Excel, and PowerPoint
- Knowledgeable in current and previous versions of the Windows operating system
- Experience with networking, firewalls, and security systems

REFERENCES

Professional and personal references available upon request.

Case Study

Part 1

You are the assistant to Gina Coletti, manager of La Dolce Vita, an Italian restaurant. She has been working on updating and formatting the lunch menu. She has asked you to complete the menu by opening the Word file **Menu**, determining how the appetizer section is formatted, and then applying the same formatting to the sections *Soups and Salads*; *Sandwiches, Calzones, and Burgers*; and *Individual Pizzas*. Save the document with the name **3-Menu**. Print and then close the document.

Part 2

Ms. Coletti has reviewed the completed menu and is pleased with it, but she wants to add a border around the entire page to increase visual interest. Open **3-Menu** and then save it with the name **3-MenuPgBorder**. Display the Borders and Shading dialog box with the Page Border tab selected and then experiment with the options available. Apply an appropriate page border to the menu. (Consider applying an art image border.) Save, print, and then close **3-MenuPgBorder**.

Part 3

Each week, the restaurant offers daily specials. Ms. Coletti has asked you to create a new menu for specials using the text in **MenuSpecials**. She has asked you to format the specials menu in a similar manner as the main menu but to change some elements to make it unique. Make the formatting changes, and then apply the same page border to the specials menu document that you applied to the main menu document. Save the document with the name **3-MenuSpecials**. Print and then close the document.

Part 4

You have been asked by the head chef to research a new recipe for an Italian dish. Using the internet, find a recipe that interests you and then prepare a Word document containing the recipe steps and ingredients. Bullet the items in the list of ingredients and number the steps in the recipe preparation. Save the document with the name **3-Recipe**. Print and then close the document.

Formatting Pages and Documents

The online course includes additional review and assessment resources.

Skills Assessment

Assessment 1 — Format a Cover Letter Document and Insert a Cover Page

1. Open **CoverLetter** and then save it with the name **4-CoverLetter**.
2. Change the left and right margins to 1.25 inches.
3. Move the insertion point to the beginning of the heading *Writing Cover Letters to People You Know* and then insert a blank page.
4. Insert a page break at the beginning of the heading *Writing Cover Letters to People You Don't Know*.
5. Move the insertion point to the beginning of the document and then insert the Filigree cover page.
6. Insert the following text in the specified fields:
   a. Type job search strategies in the *[DOCUMENT TITLE]* placeholder.
   b. Type Writing a Cover Letter in the *[Document subtitle]* placeholder.
   c. Type the current date in the *[DATE]* placeholder.
   d. Type career finders in the *[COMPANY NAME]* placeholder.
   e. Delete the *[Company address]* placeholder.
7. Move the insertion point to anywhere in the subtitle *WRITING A COVER LETTER* and then insert the Brackets 1 page numbering at the bottom of the page. (The page numbering will not appear on the cover page.)
8. Make the document active and turn on the display of nonprinting characters.
9. Move the insertion point to the blank line below the first paragraph of text (and above the page break) and then press the Delete key six times. (This deletes the page break on the first page and the page break creating a blank page 2, as well as extra blank lines.) Turn off the display of nonprinting characters.
10. Save, print, and then close **4-CoverLetter**.

Assessment 2 — Format a Photography Report into Columns

1. Open **PhotoReport** and then save it with the name **4-PhotoReport**.
2. Format the text from the first paragraph of text below the title to the end of the document into two columns with a line between and with 0.4 inch between columns.
3. Create a drop cap with the first letter of the first paragraph below the title. Specify that the drop cap is in the paragraph rather than the margin and is dropped two lines.
4. Move the insertion point to the end of the document and then insert a continuous section break to balance the columns on the second page.
5. Manually hyphenate the document. (Do not hyphenate headings and names.)
6. Save, print, and then close **4-PhotoReport**.

Assessment 3

Format an Intellectual Property Report and Insert Headers and Footers

1. Open **ProtectIssues** and then save it with the name **4-ProtectIssues**.
2. Insert a page break at the beginning of the heading *REFERENCES* (on the second page).
3. Change the top margin to 1.5 inches.
4. Change the page layout to landscape orientation.
5. Move the insertion point to the beginning of the document and then insert the Retrospect footer. Select the name at the left side of the footer and then type your first and last names.
6. Save the document and then print only page 1.
7. Change the page layout back to portrait orientation.
8. Apply the Moderate page margins.
9. Remove the footer.
10. Insert the Ion (Dark) header.
11. Insert the Ion (Dark) footer. Type property protection issues as the title and make sure your first and last names display at the right side of the footer.
12. Select the footer text (document name and your name), apply bold formatting, and then change the font size to 8 points.
13. Insert the DRAFT 1 watermark in the document.
14. Apply the Green, Accent 6, Lighter 80% page background color (last column, second row).
15. Save and then print **4-ProtectIssues**.
16. With the document still open, change the paper size to Legal (8.5 inches by 14 inches).
17. Save the document with Save As and name it **4-ProtectIssues-Legal**.
18. Check with your instructor to determine if you can print legal-sized documents. If so, print page 1 of the document.
19. Save and then close **4-ProtectIssues-Legal**.

Assessment 4

Format a Real Estate Agreement

1. Open **REAgrmnt** and then save it with the name **4-REAgrmnt**.
2. Find all occurrences of *BUYER* (matching the case) and replace them with *James Berman*.
3. Find all occurrences of *SELLER* (matching the case) and replace them with *Mona Trammell*.
4. Find all word forms of the word *buy* and replace them with *purchase*.
5. Insert Plain Number 2 page numbering at the bottom center of the page.
6. Insert a page border with the following specifications:
   - Choose the first double-line border in the *Style* list box.
   - Change the color of the page border to the standard dark red color.
   - Change the width of the page border to 1 1/2 points.
7. Display the Border and Shading Options dialog box for the page border and then change the top, left, bottom, and right measurements to 30 points. ***Hint: Display the Border and Shading Options dialog box by clicking the Options button at the Borders and Shading dialog box with the Page Border tab selected.***
8. Save, print, and then close **4-REAgrmnt**.

Visual Benchmark

Format a Resume Styles Report

1. Open **Resumes** and then save it with the name **4-Resumes**.
2. Format the document so it appears as shown in Figure 4.1 with the following specifications:
   a. Change the top margin to 1.5 inches.
   b. Change the line spacing for the entire document to 1.5 lines.
   c. Apply the Heading 1 style to the title and the Heading 2 style to the headings.
   d. Apply the Lines (Simple) style set.
   e. Apply the Savon theme.
   f. Apply the Blue Green theme colors.
   g. Change the paragraph spacing after the title to 9 points. Apply 6 points of paragraph spacing after the three headings.
   h. Insert the Austin cover page. Insert text in the placeholders and delete the Abstract placeholder as shown in the figure. (If a name appears in the author placeholder, delete it and then type your first and last names.)
   i. Insert the Ion (Dark) header and the Ion (Dark) footer.
3. Save, print, and then close **4-Resumes**.

Figure 4.1 Visual Benchmark

continues

Figure 4.1 Visual Benchmark—*continued*

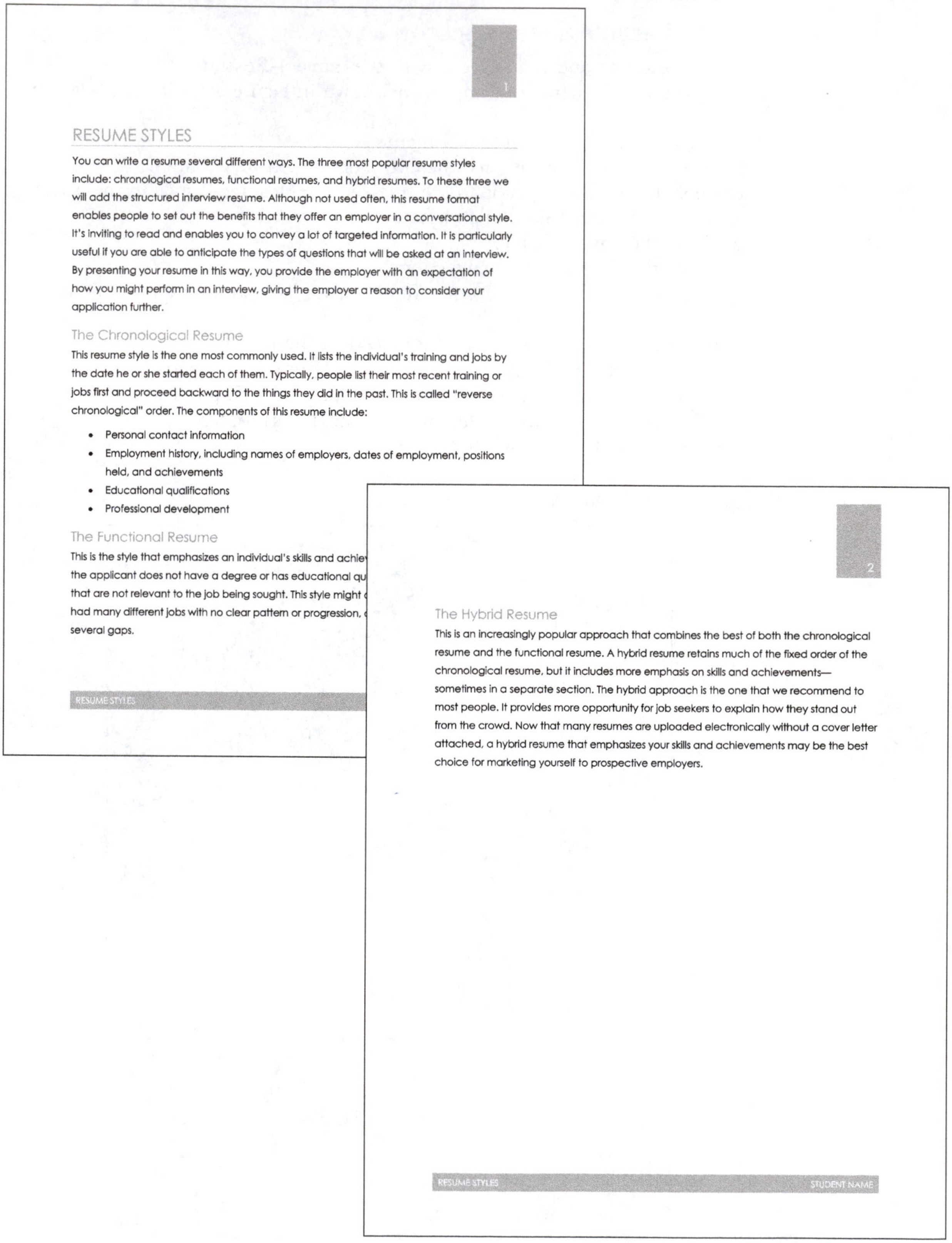

1

RESUME STYLES

You can write a resume several different ways. The three most popular resume styles include: chronological resumes, functional resumes, and hybrid resumes. To these three we will add the structured interview resume. Although not used often, this resume format enables people to set out the benefits that they offer an employer in a conversational style. It's inviting to read and enables you to convey a lot of targeted information. It is particularly useful if you are able to anticipate the types of questions that will be asked at an interview. By presenting your resume in this way, you provide the employer with an expectation of how you might perform in an interview, giving the employer a reason to consider your application further.

The Chronological Resume

This resume style is the one most commonly used. It lists the individual's training and jobs by the date he or she started each of them. Typically, people list their most recent training or jobs first and proceed backward to the things they did in the past. This is called "reverse chronological" order. The components of this resume include:

- Personal contact information
- Employment history, including names of employers, dates of employment, positions held, and achievements
- Educational qualifications
- Professional development

The Functional Resume

This is the style that emphasizes an individual's skills and achie
the applicant does not have a degree or has educational qu
that are not relevant to the job being sought. This style might
had many different jobs with no clear pattern or progression,
several gaps.

RESUME STYLES

2

The Hybrid Resume

This is an increasingly popular approach that combines the best of both the chronological resume and the functional resume. A hybrid resume retains much of the fixed order of the chronological resume, but it includes more emphasis on skills and achievements—sometimes in a separate section. The hybrid approach is the one that we recommend to most people. It provides more opportunity for job seekers to explain how they stand out from the crowd. Now that many resumes are uploaded electronically without a cover letter attached, a hybrid resume that emphasizes your skills and achievements may be the best choice for marketing yourself to prospective employers.

RESUME STYLES STUDENT NAME

Case Study

Part 1

You work for Citizens for Consumer Safety, a nonprofit organization that provides information on household safety. Your supervisor, Melinda Johansson, has asked you to format a document on smoke detectors. She will use the document as an informational handout during a presentation on smoke detectors. Open **SmokeDetectors** and then save it with the name **4-SmokeDetectors-1**. Apply a style set, apply appropriate styles to the title and headings, and then apply a theme and theme colors to the document. Ms. Johansson has asked you to change the page layout to landscape orientation and to change the left and right margins to 1.5 inches. She wants to allow extra space at the left and right margins so audience members can write notes in these areas. Use the Help feature or experiment with the options in the Header & Footer Tools Design tab and figure out how to put page numbers on every page but the first page. Insert page numbers in the document that print at the top right of every page except the first page. Save, print, and then close **4-SmokeDetectors-1**.

Part 2

After reviewing the formatted document on smoke detectors, Ms. Johansson has decided that she would like it to print in the default orientation (portrait) and that she would like to see different theme and style choices. She has also decided that the term *smoke alarm* should be replaced with *smoke detector*. She has asked you to open and then make changes to the original document. Open **SmokeDetectors** and then save it with the name **4-SmokeDetectors-2**. Apply styles to the title and headings and apply a theme and theme colors to the document (other than the one you chose for Part 1). Search for all occurrences of *Smoke Alarm* and replace them with *Smoke Detector* matching the case. Search for all occurrences of *smoke alarm* and replace them with *smoke detector* without matching the case. Insert a cover page of your choosing and then insert the appropriate information in the page. Use the current date and your name as the author and delete all unused placeholders. Use the Help feature or experiment with the options in the Header & Footer Tools Design tab and figure out how to insert odd-page and even-page footers in a document. Insert an odd-page footer that prints the page number at the right margin and insert an even-page footer that prints the page number at the left margin. You do not want the footer to print on the cover page, so make sure you position the insertion point below the cover page before inserting the footers. Make any other formatting changes to improve the appearance and layout of the document. Save, print, and then close **4-SmokeDetectors-2**.

Part 3

Ms. Johansson has asked you to prepare a document on infant car seats and car seat safety to be available for distribution at a local community center. Find websites that provide information on child and infant car seats and car seat safety. Using the information you find, write a report that covers at least the following topics:

- Description of types of infant car seats (such as rear-facing, convertible, forward-facing, built-in, and booster)
- Safety rules and guidelines for safe installation
- Websites that sell infant car seats, along with price ranges for specific models
- Price ranges
- Websites that provide safety information

Format the report using styles and a theme and include a cover page and headers and/or footers. Save the completed document and name it **4-CarSeats**. Print and then close the document.

Unit 1 Performance Assessment

Data Files

Before beginning unit work, copy the WL1U1 folder to your storage medium and then make WL1U1 the active folder.

Assessing Proficiency

In this unit, you have learned to create, edit, save, and print Word documents. You have also learned to format characters, paragraphs, pages, and documents.

Assessment 1

Format a Document on Website Design

1. Open **Website** and then save it with the name **U1-Website**.
2. Complete a spelling and grammar check.
3. Select the text from the paragraph that begins *Make your home page work for you.* through the end of the document and then apply bulleted formatting.
4. Select and then apply bold formatting to the first sentence of each bulleted paragraph.
5. Apply a single-line bottom border to the document title and apply Gold, Accent 4, Lighter 80% paragraph shading (eighth column, second row in the *Theme Colors* section) to the title.
6. Save and then print **U1-Website**.
7. Change the top, left, and right margins to 1.5 inches.
8. Select the bulleted paragraphs, change the paragraph alignment to justified, and then apply numbered formatting.
9. Select the entire document and then change the font to 12-point Cambria.
10. Insert the text shown in Figure U1.1 after paragraph number 2. (The number *3.* should automatically be inserted preceding the text you type.)
11. Save, print, and then close **U1-Website**.

Figure U1.1 Assessment 1

Avoid a cluttered look. In design, less is more. Strive for a clean look to your pages, using ample margins and white space.

Assessment 2 Format an Accumulated Returns Document

1. Open **TotalReturns** and then save it with the name **U1-TotalReturns**.
2. Select the entire document and then make the following changes:
   a. Apply the No Spacing style.
   b. Change the line spacing to 1.5 lines.
   c. Change the font to 12-point Cambria.
   d. Apply 6 points of spacing after paragraphs.
3. Select the title *TOTAL RETURN CHARTS*, change the font to 14-point Corbel bold, change the alignment to centered, and apply Blue-Gray, Text 2, Lighter 80% paragraph shading (fourth column, second row in the *Theme Colors* section).
4. Apply bold formatting to the following text that appears at the beginnings of the second through the fifth paragraphs:
   Average annual total return:
   Annual total return:
   Accumulation units:
   Accumulative rates:
5. Select the paragraphs of text in the body of the document (all paragraphs except the title) and then change the paragraph alignment to justified.
6. Select the paragraphs that begin with the bolded words, sort the paragraphs in ascending order, and then indent the text 0.5 inch from the left margin.
7. Insert a watermark that prints *DRAFT* diagonally across the page.
8. Save, print, and then close **U1-TotalReturns**.

Assessment 3 Format a Computer Ethics Report

1. Open **FutureEthics** and then save it with the name **U1-FutureEthics**.
2. Apply the Heading 1 style to the titles *FUTURE OF COMPUTER ETHICS* and *REFERENCES*.
3. Apply the Heading 2 style to the headings in the document.
4. Apply the Shaded style set.
5. Apply the Open paragraph spacing.
6. Apply the Parallax theme and then change the theme fonts to Garamond.
7. Center the two titles (*FUTURE OF COMPUTER ETHICS* and *REFERENCES*).
8. Add 6 points of paragraph spacing after each title and heading with the Heading 1 or Heading 2 style applied.
9. Create a hanging indent for the paragraphs of text below the title *REFERENCES*.
10. Insert page numbers that print at the bottom center of each page.
11. Save, print, and then close **U1-FutureEthics**.

Assessment 4 Set Tabs and Type Income by Division Text in Columns

1. At a new blank document, type the text shown in Figure U1.2 with the following specifications:
   a. Apply bold formatting to and center the title as shown.
   b. You determine the tab settings for the text in columns.
   c. Select the entire document and then change the font to 12-point Arial.
2. Save the document with the name **U1-Income**.
3. Print and then close **U1-Income**.

Figure U1.2 Assessment 4

INCOME BY DIVISION

	2019	**2020**	**2021**
Public Relations	$14,375	$16,340	$16,200
Database Services	9,205	15,055	13,725
Graphic Design	18,400	21,790	19,600
Technical Support	5,780	7,325	9,600

Assessment 5

Set Tabs and Type Table of Contents Text

1. At a blank document, type the text shown in Figure U1.3 with the following specifications:
   a. Apply bold formatting to and center the title as shown.
   b. You determine the tab settings for the text in columns.
   c. Select the entire document, change the font to 12-point Cambria, and then change the line spacing to 1.5 lines.
2. Save the document with the name **U1-TofC**.
3. Print and then close **U1-TofC**.

Figure U1.3 Assessment 5

TABLE OF CONTENTS

Online Shopping..2
Online Services..4
Peer-to-Peer Online Transactions.......................................5
Transaction Payment Methods...8
Transaction Security and Encryption.................................11
Establishing a Website...14

Assessment

Format a Union Agreement Contract

1. Open **LaborContract** and then save it with the name **U1-LaborContract**.
2. Find all occurrences of *REINBERG MANUFACTURING* and replace them with *MILLWOOD ENTERPRISES*.
3. Find all occurrences of *RM* and replace them with *ME*.
4. Find all occurrences of *LABOR WORKERS' UNION* and replace them with *SERVICE EMPLOYEES' UNION*.
5. Find all occurrences of *LWU* and replace them with *SEU*.
6. Select the entire document and then change the font to 12-point Cambria and the line spacing to double spacing.
7. Select the numbered paragraphs in the section *Transfers and Moving Expenses* and change them to bulleted paragraphs.

8. Select the numbered paragraphs in the section *Sick Leave* and change them to bulleted paragraphs.
9. Change to landscape orientation and change the top margin to 1.5 inches.
10. Save and then print **U1-LaborContract**.
11. Change to portrait orientation and change the left margin (previously the top margin) back to 1 inch.
12. Insert the Whisp cover page and then insert the current date in the date placeholder, the title *Union Agreement* as the document title, and *Millwood Enterprises* as the document subtitle. Select the author placeholder (or the name) at the bottom of the cover page and then type your first and last names. Delete the company name placeholder.
13. Move the insertion point to the page after the cover page, insert the Ion (Dark) footer, and then make sure *UNION AGREEMENT* displays in the title placeholder and your name displays in the author placeholder. If not, type UNION AGREEMENT in the title placeholder and your first and last names in the author placeholder.
14. Save, print, and then close **U1-LaborContract**.

Assessment 7 Copy and Paste Text in a Health Plan Document

1. Open **KeyLifePlan** and then save it with the name **U1-KeyLifePlan**.
2. Open **PlanOptions** and then display the Clipboard task pane. Make sure the Clipboard is empty.
3. Select the heading *Plan Highlights* and the six paragraphs of text below it and then copy the selected text to the Clipboard.
4. Select the heading *Plan Options* and the two paragraphs of text below it (the second paragraph flows onto the next page) and then copy the selected text to the Clipboard.
5. Select the heading *Quality Assessment* and the six paragraphs of text below it and then copy the selected text to the Clipboard.
6. Close **PlanOptions**.
7. With **U1-KeyLifePlan** open, display the Clipboard task pane.
8. Move the insertion point to the beginning of the heading *Provider Network*, paste the *Plan Options* item from the Clipboard, and merge the formatting.
9. With the insertion point positioned at the beginning of the heading *Provider Network*, paste the *Plan Highlights* item from the Clipboard and then merge the formatting.
10. Move the insertion point to the beginning of the heading *Plan Options*, paste the *Quality Assessment* item from the Clipboard, and then merge the formatting.
11. Clear the Clipboard and then close it.
12. Apply the Heading 1 style to the title *KEY LIFE HEALTH PLAN*.
13. Apply the Heading 2 style to the four headings in the document.
14. Change the top margin to 1.5 inches.
15. Apply the Lines (Simple) style set.
16. Apply the Compact paragraph spacing.
17. Apply the Red Orange theme colors.
18. Insert a double-line page border in the standard dark red color.
19. Insert the Slice 1 header.
20. Insert the Slice footer and type your first and last names in the author placeholder.
21. Insert a page break at the beginning of the heading *Plan Highlights*.
22. Save, print, and then close **U1-KeyLifePlan**.

Assessment 8

Format a Bioinformatics Document

1. Open **Bioinformatics** and then save it with the name **U1-Bioinformatics**.
2. Change the line spacing for the entire document to 1.5 spacing.
3. Insert a continuous section break at the beginning of the first paragraph of text (the paragraph that begins *Bioinformatics is the mixed application*).
4. Format the text below the section break into two columns.
5. Balance the columns on the second page.
6. Create a drop cap with the first letter of the first word *Bioinformatics* that begins the first paragraph of text. Specify that the drop cap is in the paragraph and not the margin and make the drop cap two lines in height.
7. Manually hyphenate the words in the document.
8. Insert page numbers at the bottoms of the pages using the Thin Line page numbering option. (The Thin Line page number option is located in the *Plain Number* section of the Page Number button side menu.)
9. Save, print, and then close **U1-Bioinformatics**.

Assessment

Create and Format a Resume

1. Open **Resume** and then save it with the name **U1-Resume**.
2. Apply the following formatting so your document appears as shown in Figure U1.4:
   a. Change the font for the entire document to Candara.
   b. Change the top margin measurement to 1.25 inches.
   c. Apply character and paragraph formatting as shown (including bold formatting, paragraph alignment, bulleted formatting, borders and shading formatting, and adding leaders to the right tab in the *PROFESSIONAL EXPERIENCE* section, as shown in the figure).
3. Save, print, and then close **U1-Resume**.

Figure U1.4 Assessment 9

KIERNAN O'MALLEY

1533 Baylor Street East, Auburn, WA 98020 (253) 555-3912

NETWORK ADMINISTRATION PROFESSIONAL
Pursuing **CCNA Cloud certification** and **Network+** credentials
Proficient in Microsoft Office applications in Windows environment

EDUCATION

Information Systems (IS), Western Washington University, Bellingham, WA...................... 2021
Medical Specialist, Seattle University, Seattle, WA ....2017 to 2020
Medical Terminology, Green River Community College, Auburn, WA.................................2016

APPLIED RESEARCH PROJECTS

Completed **Applied Research Projects (ARPs),** in conjunction with IS degree requirements, covering all aspects of design and management of organizational technical resources, as follows:

- **Organizational Culture and Leadership** (2021): Evaluated the organizational culture of Bellevue Surgery Center's endoscopy unit and operating room (OR) in order to ensure that the mission and vision statements were being appropriately applied at the staff level.
- **Human Resources (HR) Management** (2021): Established a comprehensive orientation package for the Bellevue Surgery Center's clinical staff.
- **Strategic Management and Planning** (2020): Conducted internal/external environmental assessments in order to identify an approach for Bellevue Surgery Center to expand its OR facilities.
- **Financial Accounting** (2020): Created a quarterly operating budget for the Bellevue Surgery Center and implemented an expenditure tracking system.
- **Database Management Systems** (2019): Created an inventory-control system that optimizes inventory maintenance in a cost-effective manner.
- **Statistics and Research Analysis** (2019): Generated graphics to illustrate the Valley Hospital's assisted-reproduction success rate.
- **Management Support System** (2018): Identified solutions to resolve inventory-control vulnerabilities at minimal cost for Valley Hospital.

PROFESSIONAL EXPERIENCE

CERTIFIED SURGICAL TECHNOLOGIST

Bellevue Surgery Center, Bellevue, WA..2019 to present
Valley Hospital, Renton, WA .... 2017 to 2019
Kenmore Ambulatory Surgery Center, Kenmore, WA ....2015 to 2017
South Sound Medical Center, Auburn, WA.. 2014 to 2015

Writing Activities

The following activities give you the opportunity to practice your writing skills and to demonstrate your understanding of some of the important Word features you have mastered in this unit. Use correct grammar, appropriate word choices, and clear sentence construction. Follow the steps in Figure U1.5 to improve your writing skills.

Activity 1

Write Steps on Using KeyTips

Explore the three buttons in the Editing group on the Home tab. Learn what functions are performed by each button. At a blank document, write a paragraph describing the functions performed by each button. After writing the paragraph, add steps on how to find text using the Navigation pane. Save the completed document with the name **U1-EditingGroupButtons**. Print and then close **U1-EditingGroupButtons**.

Activity 2

Write Information on Advanced Word Options

Use Word's Help feature and the search text *word options advanced* to learn how to customize display options at the Word Options dialog box with the *Advanced* option selected. After learning about the display options, create a document that describes the steps to change the display of the *Show this number of Recent Documents* option to *10*. Assume that the steps begin at a blank document. Describe the steps to turn on the *Quickly access this number of Recent Documents* option and change the number to *6*. Again, assume that the steps begin at a blank document. Add any additional information, such as a title, heading, and/or explanatory text, that helps the reader understand the contents of the document. Save the completed document and name it **U1-DisplayOptions**. Print and then close **U1-DisplayOptions**.

Internet Research

Research Business Desktop Computer Systems

You hold a part-time job at the local chamber of commerce, where you assist the office manager, Ryan Woods. Mr. Woods will be purchasing new desktop computers for the office staff. He has asked you to research using the internet and identify at least three PCs that can be purchased directly over the internet, and he wants you to put your research and recommendations in writing. Mr. Woods is looking for solid, reliable, economical, and powerful desktop computers with good warranties and service plans. He has given you a budget of $800 per unit.

Search the internet for three desktop PC systems from three different manufacturers. Consider price, specifications (processor speed, amount of RAM, hard drive space, and monitor type and size), performance, warranties, and service plans when choosing the systems. Print your research findings and include them with your report.

Using Word, write a brief report in which you summarize the capabilities and qualities of each of the three computer systems you recommend. Include a final paragraph detailing which system you suggest for purchase and why. If possible, incorporate user opinions and/or reviews about this system to support your decision. Format your report using the concepts and techniques you learned in Unit 1. Save the report with the name **U1-InternetResearch**. Print and then close the file.

Figure U1.5 The Writing Process

The Writing Process

Plan Gather ideas, select which information to include, and choose the order in which to present the information.

Checkpoints
- What is the purpose?
- What information does the reader need to reach your intended conclusion?

Write Following the information plan and keeping the reader in mind, draft the document using clear, direct sentences that say what you mean.

Checkpoints
- What subpoints support each main thought?
- How can you connect paragraphs so the reader moves smoothly from one idea to the next?

Revise Improve what is written by changing, deleting, rearranging, or adding words, sentences, and paragraphs.

Checkpoints
- Is the meaning clear?
- Do the ideas follow a logical order?
- Have you included any unnecessary information?
- Have you built your sentences around strong nouns and verbs?

Edit Check spelling, sentence construction, word use, punctuation, and capitalization.

Checkpoints
- Can you spot any redundancies or clichés?
- Can you reduce any phrases to effective words (for example, change *the fact that* to *because*)?
- Have you used commas only where there is a strong reason for doing so?
- Did you proofread the document for errors that your spelling checker cannot identify?

Publish Prepare a final copy that can be reproduced and shared with others.

Checkpoints
- Which design elements, such as bold formatting and different fonts, will help highlight important ideas or sections?
- Will charts or other graphics help clarify meaning?

Microsoft®

Word Level 1

Unit 2

Enhancing and Customizing Documents

Microsoft® Word
Review and Assessment

Inserting and Formatting Objects

The online course includes additional review and assessment resources.

Skills Assessment

Assessment 1 Add Visual Interest to a Report on Intellectual Property

1. Open **ProtectIssues** and then save it with the name **5-ProtectIssues**.
2. Insert the **Hacker** image file from your WL1C5 folder. (Do this by clicking the Pictures button on the Insert tab.)
3. Format the image with the following specifications:
   a. Change the height to 1 inch.
   b. Change the color of the image to Blue, Accent color 1 Light (second column, third row in the *Recolor* section).
   c. Correct the contrast to Brightness: 0% (Normal) Contrast: +20% (third column, fourth row in the *Brightness/Contrast* section).
   d. Change the position of the image to Position in Middle Left with Square Text Wrapping (first column, second row in the *With Text Wrapping* section).
   e. Use the Rotate button in the Arrange group to flip the image horizontally.
4. Move the insertion point to the beginning of the paragraph immediately below the heading *Intellectual Property Protection* (on the second page). Insert the Austin Quote text box and then make the following customizations:
   a. Type the following text in the text box: "Plagiarism may be punished by law, and in many educational institutions it can result in suspension or even expulsion."
   b. Select the text and then change the font size to 11 points.
   c. Change the width of the text box to 2.8 inches.
   d. Change the position of the text box to Position in Top Center with Square Text Wrapping (second column, first row in the *With Text Wrapping* section).
5. Press Ctrl + End to move the insertion point to the end of the document.
6. Insert the Plaque shape (tenth column, second row in the *Basic Shapes* section) at the location of the insertion point and then make the following customizations:
   a. Change the shape height to 1.4 inches and the shape width to 3.9 inches.
   b. Use the Align button in the Arrange group to distribute the shape horizontally.
   c. Apply the Subtle Effect - Blue, Accent 1 shape style (second column, fourth row).
   d. Type the text Felicité Compagnie inside the shape. Insert the *é* symbol at the Symbol dialog box with the *(normal text)* font selected.
   e. Use options at the Date and Time dialog box to insert the current date below *Felicité Compagnie* and the current time below the date. Make sure the date and time will not update automatically.
   f. Select the text in the shape, change the font size to 14 points, and then apply bold formatting.
7. Save, print, and then close **5-ProtectIssues**.

Assessment 2

Create a Sales Meeting Announcement

1. At a blank document, press the Enter key two times and then create WordArt with the following specifications:
   a. Insert WordArt with the option in the first column, third row of the WordArt button drop-down list (black fill, outline, hard shadow) and then type Inlet Corporation in the WordArt text box.
   b. Change the width of the WordArt text box to 6.5 inches.
   c. Use the *Transform* option from the Text Effects button in the WordArt Styles group to apply the Chevron: Up text effect (first column, second row in the *Warp* section) to the WordArt text.
2. Press Ctrl + End and then press the Enter key three times. Change the font to 18-point Candara, apply bold formatting, change to center alignment, and then type the following text, pressing the Enter key after each line of text except the fourth line:

   National Sales Meeting
   Pacific Division
   Ocean View Resort
   May 10 through May 12, 2021

3. Insert the **Ocean** image file from your WL1C5 folder and then make the following changes to the image:
   a. Crop approximately 1 inch off the bottom of the image.
   b. Apply the Brightness: +20% Contrast: 0% (Normal) correction (fourth column, third row in the *Brightness/Contrast* section).
   c. Apply the Compound Frame, Black picture style (fourth column, second row in the Pictures Styles gallery).
   d. Change the position of the image to Position in Top Center with Square Text Wrapping (second column, first row in the *With Text Wrapping* section).
   e. Change text wrapping to Behind Text.
4. Save the announcement document and name it **5-SalesMtg**.
5. Print and then close **5-SalesMtg**.

Assessment 3

Create an Announcement

1. Open **FirstAidCourse** and then save it with the name **5-FirstAidCourse**.
2. Format the announcement as shown in Figure 5.1. Insert the **FirstAid** image file from your WL1C5 folder with the following specifications:
   a. Change the text wrapping to Tight.
   b. Change the image color to Blue, Accent color 5 Light (sixth column, third row in the *Recolor* section).
   c. Correct the brightness and contrast to Brightness: 0% (Normal) Contrast: +40% (third column, bottom row in the *Brightness/Contrast* section).
   d. Size and move the image as shown in the figure.
3. Apply paragraph shading, insert the page border, and add period leaders to the right tab, as shown in Figure 5.1.
4. Save, print, and then close **5-FirstAidCourse**. (If some of the page border does not print, consider increasing the measurements at the Border and Shading Options dialog box.)

Figure 5.1 Assessment 3

First Aid at Work

The Safety Committee is offering a two-day first aid course for employees. The objective of the course is to equip employees with the essential knowledge and practical experience to enable them to carry out first aid in the workplace. Course content includes health and safety administration, handling an incident and developing an action plan, recognizing and treating injuries and illnesses, and cardio-pulmonary resuscitation (CPR).

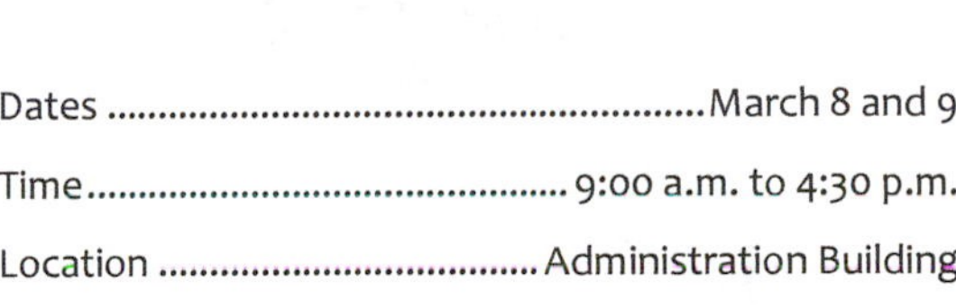

Dates .... March 8 and 9
Time .... 9:00 a.m. to 4:30 p.m.
Location .... Administration Building
Room .... Conference Room 200

Registration is available from February 15 until the course begins on March 8. Before registering, please check with your immediate supervisor to ensure that you can be excused from your normal duties for the two days.

For more information, contact Maxwell Singh at extension 3505.

Assessment 4

Insert Screen Clippings in a Memo

1. Open **FirstAidMemo** and then save it with the name **5-FirstAidMemo**.
2. Insert and format screen clippings so your document appears as shown in Figure 5.2. Use the document **FirstAidAnnounce** to create the first screen clipping, and use the document **5-FirstAidCourse** you created in Assessment 3 for the second screen clipping. ***Hint: Decrease the display percentage of the document so the entire document is visible on the screen.***
3. Move the insertion point below the screen clipping images and then insert the text as shown in the figure. Insert your initials in place of the *XX*.
4. Save, print, and then close **5-FirstAidMemo**.

Figure 5.2 Assessment 4

DATE: January 8, 2021

TO: Carmen Singleton

FROM: Maxwell Singh

SUBJECT: FIRST AID COURSE ANNOUNCEMENTS

As you requested, I have created two announcements for the first aid course in March. Please review the two announcements shown below and let me know which one you prefer.

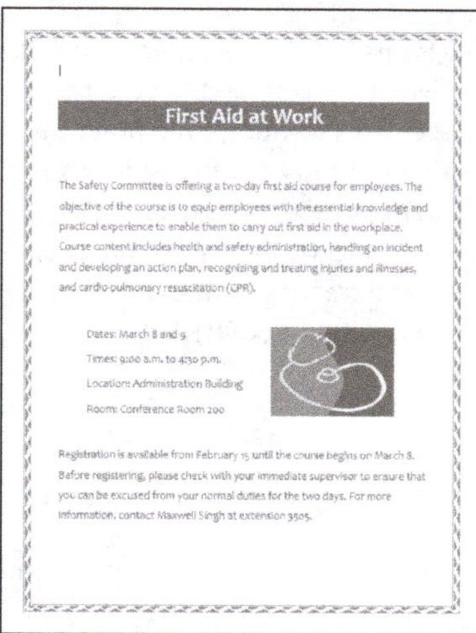

First Aid at Work

The Safety Committee is offering a two-day first aid course for employees. The objective of the course is to equip employees with the essential knowledge and practical experience to enable them to carry out first aid in the workplace. Course content includes health and safety administration, handling an incident and developing an action plan, recognizing and treating injuries and illnesses, and cardio-pulmonary resuscitation (CPR).

Dates: March 8 and 9

Times: 9:00 a.m. to 4:30 p.m.

Location: Administration Building

Room: Conference Room 200

Registration is available from February 15 until the course begins on March 8. Before registering, please check with your immediate supervisor to ensure that you can be excused from your normal duties for the two days. For more information, contact Maxwell Singh at extension 3505.

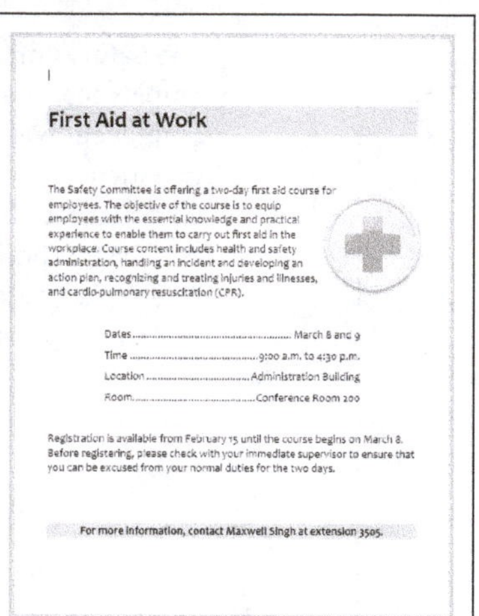

First Aid at Work

The Safety Committee is offering a two-day first aid course for employees. The objective of the course is to equip employees with the essential knowledge and practical experience to enable them to carry out first aid in the workplace. Course content includes health and safety administration, handling an incident and developing an action plan, recognizing and treating injuries and illnesses, and cardio-pulmonary resuscitation (CPR).

Dates .... March 8 and 9

Time .... 9:00 a.m. to 4:30 p.m.

Location .... Administration Building

Room .... Conference Room 200

Registration is available from February 15 until the course begins on March 8. Before registering, please check with your immediate supervisor to ensure that you can be excused from your normal duties for the two days.

For more information, contact Maxwell Singh at extension 3505.

XX
5-FirstAidMemo

Assessment 5 Create and Format a Company SmartArt Graphic

1. At a blank document, create the SmartArt graphic shown in Figure 5.3 with the following specifications:
   a. Use the Titled Matrix SmartArt graphic (second option in the *Matrix* section).
   b. Apply the Colorful - Accent Colors SmartArt style (first option in the *Colorful* section).
   c. Apply the Polished SmartArt style (first option in the *3-D* section).
   d. With the middle shape selected, apply the Intense Effect - Green, Accent 6 shape style. (Click the SmartArt Tools Format tab, click the More Shape Styles button in the Shape Styles group, and then click the last option in the *Theme Styles* section.)
   e. Type all the text shown in Figure 5.3.
   f. Select only the SmartArt graphic (not a specific shape) and then apply the WordArt option in the first column, third row of the WordArt button drop-down list to the text.
   g. Change the height of the SmartArt graphic to 3.2 inches and the width to 5.3 inches.
   h. Position the SmartArt graphic at the top center of the page with square text wrapping.
2. Save the document and name it **5-OCGraphic**.
3. Print and then close **5-OCGraphic**.

Figure 5.3 Assessment 5

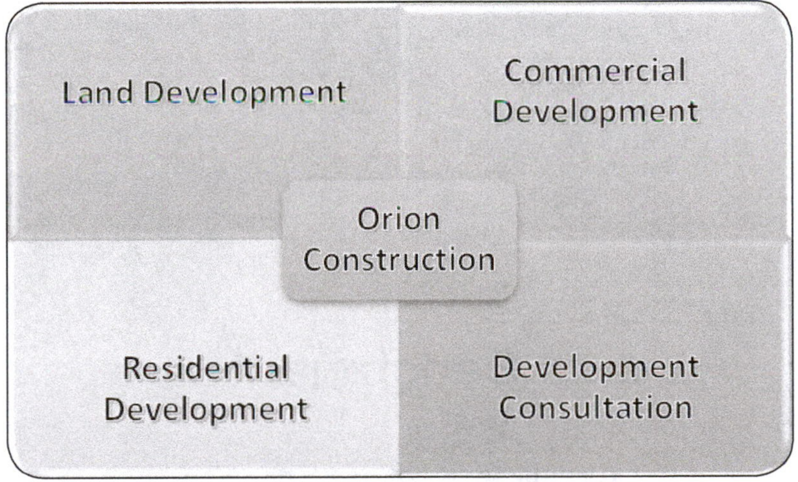

Assessment 6

Create and Format a Company Organizational Chart

1. At a blank document, create the organizational chart shown in Figure 5.4 with the following specifications:
   a. Use the Hierarchy SmartArt graphic (second column, second row with *Hierarchy* selected in the left panel).
   b. With the top text box selected, add a shape above it.
   c. Select the text box at the right in the third row and then add a shape below it.
   d. Type the text shown in the organizational chart in Figure 5.4.
   e. Apply the Colorful Range - Accent Colors 3 to 4 SmartArt style (third option in the *Colorful* section).
   f. Increase the height to 4.5 inches and the width to 6.5 inches.
   g. Position the organizational chart in the middle of the page with square text wrapping.
2. Save the document and name it **5-CoOrgChart**.
3. Print and then close **5-CoOrgChart**.

Figure 5.4 Assessment 6

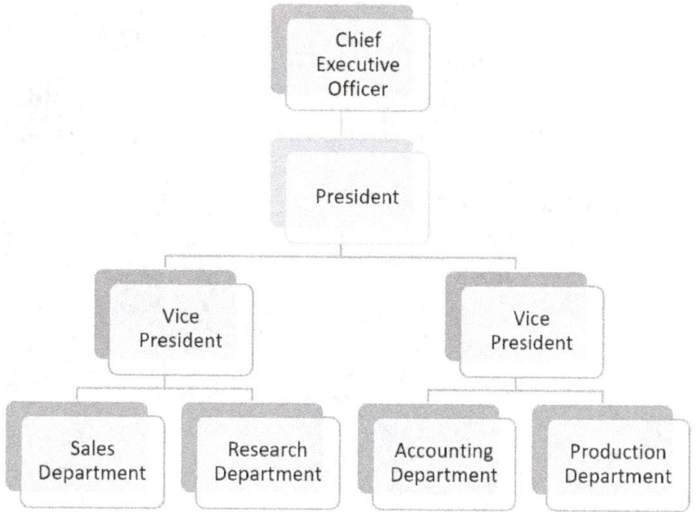

Visual Benchmark

Activity 1

Create a Flyer

1. Create the flyer shown in Figure 5.5 with the following specifications:
   - Create the title *Pugs on Parade!* as WordArt using the option in the first column, first row in the WordArt button drop-down list. Change the width to 6.5 inches, apply the Warp Up transform effect (third column, fourth row in the *Warp* section), and then change the text fill color to standard dark red.
   - Create the shape containing the text *Admission is free!* using the Explosion: 8 Points shape (first column, first row in the *Stars and Banners* section of the Shapes button drop-down list).
   - Insert the **Pug** image file from your WL1C5 folder. Change the text wrapping for the image to Behind Text and then size and position the image as shown in the figure.

- Create the line above the last line of text as a top border. Change the color to standard dark red and the width to 3 points.
- Make any other changes so your document appears similar to Figure 5.5.

2. Save the document and name it **5-PugFlyer**.
3. Print and then close the document.

Figure 5.5 Visual Benchmark 1

Pugs on Parade!

Come join us for the sixth annual "Pugs on Parade" party, Saturday, July 24, at Mercer Way Park from 1:00 to 3:30 p.m.

Admission is free!

Prizes awarded for the best costumes.

Activity 2

Format a Report

1. Open **Resume** and then save it with the name **5-Resume**.
2. Format the report so it appears as shown in Figure 5.6 with the following specifications:
   a. Insert the WordArt text *Résumé Writing* with the following specifications:
      - Use the option in the first column, third row of the WordArt button drop-down list.
      - Type the text Résumé Writing and insert the *é* symbol using the Symbol dialog box.
      - Change the position to Position in Top Center with Square Text Wrapping.
      - Change the width of the WordArt to 5.5 inches.
      - Apply the Warp Up transform text effect (third column, fourth row in the *Warp* section).

   b. Insert the pull quote with the following specifications:
      - Use the Motion Quote text box.
      - Type the text shown in the pull quote text box in Figure 5.6. (Use the Symbol dialog box to insert the two *é* symbols in the word *résumé*.)
      - Select the text box and then change the font size of the text to 11 points.
      - Change the width of the text box to 2.3 inches.
      - Position the text box in the middle center with square text wrapping.

   c. Insert the cake image with the following specifications:
      - Insert the **Cake** image file from your WL1C5 folder.
      - Change the image color to Black and White: 50% (sixth column, first row in the *Recolor* section).
      - Change the width to 0.9 inches.
      - Change the text wrapping to Tight.
      - Position the cake image as shown in Figure 5.6.
3. Save, print, and then close **5-Resume**.

Activity 3

Create and Format a SmartArt Graphic

1. At a blank document, create the document shown in Figure 5.7 (on page 42). Create and format the SmartArt graphic as shown in the figure. ***Hint: Use the* Step Up Process *graphic*.** Change the width of the SmartArt graphic to 6.5 inches. (Bold the white text with the dark blue paragraph shading. When formatting the SmartArt, you will need to change the colors of each shape separately.)
2. Save the completed document and name it **5-SalesGraphic**.
3. Print and then close **5-SalesGraphic**.

Figure 5.6 Visual Benchmark 2

Résumé Writing

To produce the best "fitting" résumé, you need to know about yourself and you need to know about the job you are applying for. Before you do anything else, ask yourself why you are preparing a résumé. The answer to this question is going to vary from one person to the next, and here are our top ten reasons for writing a résumé:

1. You have seen a job that appeals to you advertised in the paper.
2. You want to market yourself to win a contract or a proposal or be elected to a committee or organization.
3. You have seen a job that appeals to you on an internet job site.
4. Your friends or family told you of a job opening at a local company.
5. You want to work for the local company and thought that sending a résumé to them might get their attention.
6. You have seen a job advertised internally at work.
7. You are going for a promotion.
8. You are feeling fed up, and writing down all your achievements will cheer you up and might motivate you to look for a better job.
9. You are thinking "Oh, so that's a résumé! I suppose I ought to try to remember what I've been doing with my life."
10. Your company is about to be downsized and you want to update your résumé to be ready for any good opportunities.

All of these certainly are good reasons to write a résumé, but the résumé serves many different purposes. One way of seeing the different purposes is to ask yourself who is going to read the résumé in each case.

Résumés 1 through 5 will be read by potential employers who probably do not know you. Résumés 6 and 7 are likely to be read by your boss or other people who know you. Résumés 8 through 10 are really for your own benefit and should not be considered as suitable for sending out to employers.

The Right Mix

Think about the list of reasons again. How else can you divide up these reasons? An important difference is that in some cases, you will have a good idea of what the employer is looking for because you have a job advertisement in front of you and can tailor your résumé accordingly. For others, you have no idea what the reader might want to see.

"Updating your résumé from time to time is a good idea so you do not forget important details..."

Updating your résumé from time to time is a good idea so you do not forget important details, but remember that the result of such a process will not be a winning résumé. It will be a useful list of tasks and achievements.

Writing a résumé is like baking a cake. You need all the right ingredients: flour, butter, eggs, and so on. It is what you do with the ingredients that makes the difference between a great résumé (or cake) and failure. Keeping your résumé up-to-date is like keeping a stock of ingredients in the pantry—it's potentially very useful, but do not imagine that is the end of it!

Figure 5.7 Visual Benchmark 3

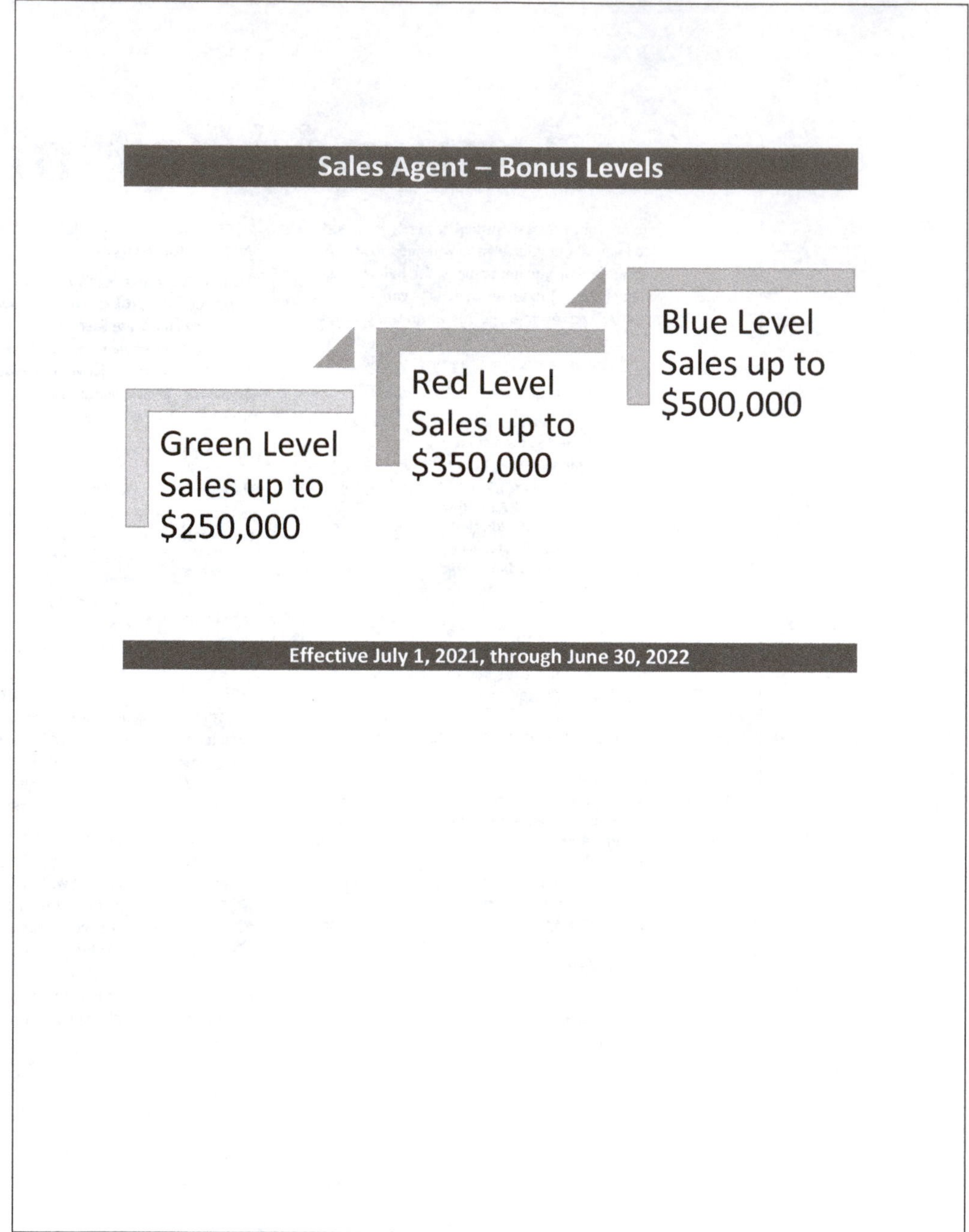

Case Study

Part 1

You work for Honoré Financial Services and have been asked by the office manager, Jason Monroe, to prepare an information newsletter. Mr. Monroe has asked you to open the document named **Budget** and then format it into columns. You are to decide the number of columns and any additional enhancements to the columns. Mr. Monroe also wants you to proofread the document and correct any spelling and grammatical errors. Save the completed newsletter, naming it **5-Budget**, and then print it. When Mr. Monroe reviews the newsletter, he decides that it needs additional visual appeal. He wants you to insert visual elements in the newsletter, such as WordArt, an image, a predesigned text box, and/or a drop cap. After adding the element(s), save, print, and then close **5-Budget**.

Part 2

Honoré Financial Services will offer a free workshop titled *Planning for Financial Success*. Mr. Monroe has asked you to prepare an announcement containing information on the workshop. You determine what to include in the announcement, such as the date, time, location, and so forth. Enhance the announcement by inserting an image and by applying formatting such as font, paragraph alignment, and borders. Save the completed document and name it **5-Announce**. Print and then close the document.

Part 3

Honoré Financial Services has adopted a new slogan and Mr. Monroe has asked you to create a shape with the new slogan inside it. Experiment with the shadow and 3-D shape effects available on the Drawing Tools Format tab and then create a shape and enhance it with shadow and/or 3-D effects. Insert the new Honoré Financial Services slogan, *Retirement Planning Made Easy*, in the shape. Include any additional enhancements to improve the visual interest of the shape and slogan. Save the completed document and name it **5-Slogan**. Print and then close the document.

Part 4

Mr. Monroe has asked you to prepare an organization chart that will become part of the company profile. Create a SmartArt organizational chart using the position titles shown in Figure 5.8. Use the order and structure in Figure 5.8 to guide the layout of the SmartArt chart. Format the organizational chart to enhance the appearance. Save the completed organizational chart document and name it **5-HFSOrgChart**. Print and then close the document.

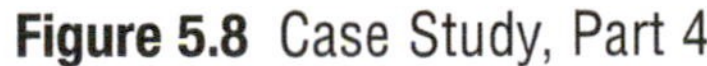

Figure 5.8 Case Study, Part 4

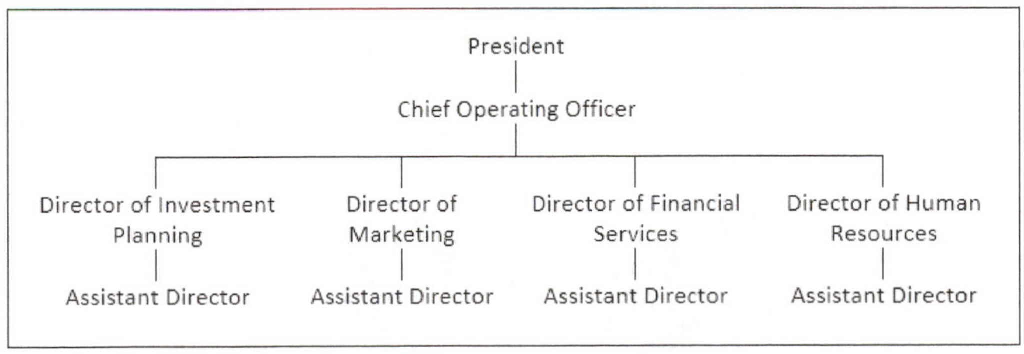

Part 5

Mr. Monroe has asked you to prepare a document containing information on teaching children how to budget. Use the internet to find websites and articles that provide information on this topic. Write a synopsis of the information and include at least four suggestions for teaching children to manage their money. Format the text into newspaper columns. Add additional enhancements to improve the appearance of the document. Save the completed document and name it **5-ChildBudget**. Print and then close the document.

CHAPTER 6

Managing Documents

The online course includes additional review and assessment resources.

Skills Assessment

Assessment 1

Manage Documents

1. Open **OMSHandbook**.
2. Change to Draft view.
3. Change to Read Mode view and then return to the document. ***Hint: To return to the document, click the View tab and then click the* Edit Document *option.***
4. Display the Immersive Learning Tools tab and then make the following changes:
   a. Change the column width to Wide.
   b. Change the page color to Sepia.
   c. If a speaker is connected to your computer, start the reading of the document.
   d. Use buttons on the playback toolbar to skip to the next paragraph, skip to the previous paragraph, change the reading voice to Microsoft Zira, and then change back to Microsoft David.
   e. Close the learning tools.
5. Change the page movement to side to side, display page thumbnails, remove the display of thumbnails, and then change page movement back to vertical.
6. Close **OMSHandbook**.
7. Open **StaffMtg**, **Agreement**, and **Robots**.
8. Make **Agreement** the active document.
9. Make **StaffMtg** the active document.
10. Arrange all the windows.
11. Make **Robots** the active document and then minimize it.
12. Minimize the remaining documents.
13. Restore **StaffMtg**.
14. Restore **Agreement**.
15. Restore **Robots**.
16. Maximize and then close **StaffMtg** and then maximize and close **Robots**.
17. Maximize **Agreement** and then save the document with the name **6-Agreement**.
18. Open **AptLease**.
19. View **6-Agreement** and **AptLease** side by side.

20. Scroll through both documents simultaneously and notice the formatting differences between the titles, headings, and fonts in the two documents. Change the font and apply shading to only the title and headings in **6-Agreement** to match the font and shading of the title and headings in **AptLease**.
21. Make **AptLease** active and then close it.
22. Save **6-Agreement**.
23. Move the insertion point to the end of the document and then insert the document **Terms**.
24. Apply formatting to the inserted text so it matches the formatting of the previous text in **6-Agreement**.
25. Move the insertion point to the end of the document and then insert the document **Signature**.
26. Save, print, and then close **6-Agreement**.

Assessment 2

Prepare an Envelope

1. At a blank document, prepare an envelope with the text shown in Figure 6.1.
2. Save the envelope document and name it **6-EnvMiller**.
3. Print and then close **6-EnvMiller**.

Assessment 3

Prepare Mailing Labels

1. Prepare mailing labels with the names and addresses shown in Figure 6.2. Use a label option of your choosing. (You may need to check with your instructor before choosing an option.) When entering a street number such as *147TH*, Word will convert the *th* to superscript letters when you press the spacebar after typing *147TH*. To remove the superscript formatting, immediately click the Undo button on the Quick Access Toolbar.
2. Save the document and name it **6-LabelsOhio**.
3. Print and then close **6-LabelsOhio**.
4. At the blank document screen, close the document without saving changes.

Figure 6.1 Assessment 2

DR ROSEANNE HOLT
21330 CEDAR DR
LOGAN UT 84598

GENE MILLER
4559 CORRIN AVE
SMITHFIELD UT 84521

Figure 6.2 Assessment 3

SUSAN LUTOVSKY 1402 MELLINGER DR FAIRHOPE OH 43209	JIM AND PAT KEIL 413 JACKSON ST AVONDALE OH 43887	IRENE HAGEN 12930 147TH AVE E CANTON OH 43296
VINCE KILEY 14005 288TH ST CANTON OH 43287	LEONARD KRUEGER 13290 N 120TH ST CANTON OH 43291	HELGA GUNDSTROM PO BOX 3112 AVONDALE OH 43887

Assessment 4

Prepare a Fax

1. Display the New backstage area, search for *fax*, and then download the Fax (Equity theme) template. (If the template is not available at the New backstage area, open the **Fax** document from your WL1C6 folder.) Insert the following information in the specified fields:

To	Frank Gallagher
From	(your first and last names)
Fax	(206) 555-9010
Pages	3
Phone	(206) 555-9005
Date	(insert current date)
Re	Consultation Agreement
CC	Jolene Yin

   Type X in the *For Review* check box.

   Comments Please review the Consultation Agreement and advise me of any legal issues.
2. Save the document and name it **6-Fax**.
3. Print and then close the document.

Assessment 5

Save a Document as a Web Page

1. Experiment with the *Save as type* option box at the Save As dialog box and figure out how to save a document as a single-file web page.
2. Open **NSS**, display the Save As dialog box, and then change the *Save as type* option to *Single File Web Page*. Click the Change Title button in the Save As dialog box. At the Enter Text dialog box, type Northland Security Systems in the *Page title* text box and then click OK to close the dialog box. Click the Save button in the Save As dialog box.
3. Close the **NSS** web page file.
4. Open your web browser and then open the **NSS** web page file. (If necessary, check with your instructor to determine the specific steps on opening the web browser and opening the file.)
5. Close your web browser.

Assessment 6

Prepare Personal Mailing Labels

1. At a blank document, type your name and address and then apply formatting to enhance the appearance of the text. (You determine the font, font size, and font color.)
2. Create labels with your name and address. (You determine the label vendor and product number.)
3. Save the label document and name it **6-PersonalLabels**.
4. Print and then close the document.
5. Close the document containing your name and address without saving the changes.

Assessment 7

Save a Template; Open a Document Based on the Template

1. Open **Labels** and then save it as a Word Template in your WL1C6 folder and name the template **6-LabelsTemplate**.
2. Close **6-LabelsTemplate**.
3. Open File Explorer and then open a document based on the **6-LabelsTemplate** template document.
4. Click in the *Name* content control and then type Jack Stiles. (When you click in the Street Address content control in the next step, Word will automatically update the name on all labels.)
5. Click in the *Street Address* content control and then type 4493 Second Street. (When you click in the City, ST ZIP Code content control in the next step, Word will automatically update the street address on all labels.)
6. Click in the *City, ST ZIP Code* content control and then type Stowe, VT 05661.
7. Click anywhere in the label document and Word will automatically update the city, state, and zip code in all labels.
8. Save the completed document and name it **6-StilesLabels**.
9. Print and then close **6-StilesLabels**.

Assessment 8

Download and Complete an Award Certificate

1. Display the New backstage area and then search for and download a certificate of your choosing. (Type certificate in the search text box and then download a certificate that interests you.)
2. Insert the appropriate information in the certificate placeholders or content controls.
3. Save the completed certificate and name the document **6-Certificate**.
4. Print and then close the document.

Visual Benchmark

Activity 1

Prepare Custom Labels

1. You can create a sheet of labels with the same information in each label by typing the information in the *Address* text box at the Envelopes and Labels dialog box. Or you can type the information, select it, and then create the label. Using this technique, create the sheet of labels shown in Figure 6.3 with the following specifications:
   - Open **NSSLabels**.
   - Set the text in 12-point Magneto.
   - Select the entire document and then create the labels using the Avery US Letter label vendor and the 5161 product number.

Figure 6.3 Visual Benchmark 1

2. Save the labels document and name it **6-NSSLabels**.
3. Print and then close the document.
4. Close **NSSLabels** without saving it.

Activity 2

Create an Invitation

1. Open File Explorer and then open a document based on the template **GalaTemplate** located in your WL1C6 folder.
2. Type the text in the appropriate content controls as shown in the figure.
3. Change the color of the text *Annual Garden Gala* to Blue (eighth color in the *Standard Colors* section).
4. Change the color of the date and time text to Olive Green, Accent 3, Darker 25% (seventh column, fifth row in the *Theme Colors* section).
5. Insert the **Flowers** image file from your WL1C6 folder with the following specifications:
   - Change the text wrapping to behind the text.
   - Set the light background as transparent. ***Hint: Use the* Set Transparent Color *option from the* Color *button on the* Picture Tools Format *tab.***
   - Size and position the image so it appears as shown in Figure 6.4.
6. Save the invitation and name it **6-Gala**.

7. Save the invitation document as a PDF file with the same name.
8. Open the **6-Gala** file in Adobe Acrobat Reader, print the file, and then close Adobe Acrobat Reader.
9. Save and then close the **6-Gala** document.

Figure 6.4 Visual Benchmark 2

Case Study

Part 1

You are the office manager for a real estate company, Macadam Realty, and have been asked by the senior sales associate, Lucy Hendricks, to prepare mailing labels for the company. Include on the labels the company name, Macadam Realty, and the address, 100 Third Street, Suite 210, Denver, CO 80803. Use a decorative font for the name and address and make the *M* in *Macadam* and the *R* in *Realty* larger and more pronounced than the surrounding text. Save the completed document and name it **6-RELabels**. Print and then close the document.

Part 2

One of your responsibilities at Macadam Realty is to format contract forms. Open **REConAgrmnt** and then save it with the name **6-REConAgrmnt**. Ms. Hendricks has asked you to insert signature information at the end of the document using the file named **RESig**. With **6-REConAgrmnt** still open, open **REBuildAgrmnt**. Format **6-REConAgrmnt** so it is formatted in a manner similar to **REBuildAgrmnt**. Consider the following when specifying formatting: fonts, font sizes, and paragraph shading. Save, print, and then close **6-REConAgrmnt**. Close **REBuildAgrmnt**.

Part 3

Ms. Hendricks has asked you to insert document properties in **REBuildAgrmnt** and **6-REConAgrmnt**. Use the Help feature to learn how to insert document properties. With the information you learn from the Help feature, open each document separately, display the Info backstage area, click the Show All Properties hyperlink (you may need to scroll down the backstage area to locate this hyperlink), and then insert document properties in the following fields (you determine the information to type): *Title*, *Categories*, *Subject*, and *Company*. Print the document properties for each document. (Change the first gallery in the *Settings* category in the Print backstage area to *Document Info*.) Save each document with the original name and then close the documents.

Part 4

A client of the real estate company, Anna Hurley, is considering purchasing several rental properties and has asked for information on how to locate real estate rental forms. Using the internet, locate at least three websites that offer real estate rental forms. Write a letter to Anna Hurley at 2300 South 22nd Street, Denver, CO 80205. In the letter, list the websites you found and include information on which site you thought offered the most resources. Also include in the letter that Macadam Realty is very interested in helping her locate and purchase rental properties. Save the document and name it **6-RELtr**. Create an envelope for the letter and add it to the letter document. Save, print, and then close **6-RELtr**. (You may need to manually feed the envelope into the printer.)

Microsoft® Word
Review and Assessment

Creating Tables

The online course includes additional review and assessment resources.

Skills Assessment

Assessment 1

Create, Format, and Modify a Training Schedule Table

1. At a blank document, create a table with four columns and five rows.
2. Type text in the cells as shown in Figure 7.1.
3. Insert a new column at the right side of the table and then type the following text in the new cells:

   Trainer
   Marsden
   Trujillo
   Yong
   Stein

4. Change the widths of the columns to the following measurements:

   First column = 0.8 inch
   Second column = 1.2 inches
   Third column = 0.7 inch
   Fourth column = 1.3 inches
   Fifth column = 0.9 inch

5. Insert a new row above the first row and then, with the new row selected, merge the cells. Type APPLICATION TRAINING SCHEDULE in the cell and then center-align the text.
6. Select the second row (contains the text *Section*, *Training*, *Days*, and so on) and then apply bold formatting to and center-align the text.
7. Display the Table Tools Design tab, apply the Grid Table 4 table style (first column, fourth row in the *Grid Tables* section), and then remove the check mark from the *First Column* check box.
8. Horizontally center the table on the page. ***Hint: Do this at the Table Properties dialog box with the Table tab selected.***
9. Save the document and name it **7-SchTable**.
10. Print and then close **7-SchTable**.

Figure 7.1 Assessment 1

Section	Training	Days	Time
WD100	Word Level 1	MWF	9:00 to 10:00 a.m.
WD110	Word Level 2	TTh	1:30 to 3:00 p.m.
EX100	Excel Level 1	MTW	3:00 to 4:00 p.m.
EX110	Excel Level 2	TTh	2:00 to 3:30 p.m.

Assessment 2 — Create, Format, and Modify a Property Replacement Costs Table

1. At a blank document, create a table with two columns and six rows.
2. Type the text in the cells in the table as shown in Figure 7.2. (Press the Enter key after typing the word *PROPERTY* in the first cell.)
3. Merge the cells in the top row and then center-align the text in the merged cell.
4. Right-align the text in the cells containing money amounts and the blank cell below the last amount (cells B2 through B6).
5. Click in the *Accounts receivable* cell and then insert a row below it. Type Equipment in the new cell at the left and type $83,560 in the new cell at the right.
6. Insert a formula in cell B7 that sums the amounts in cells B2 through B6 and then change the number format to *#,##0*. Type a dollar symbol ($) before the amount in cell B7.
7. Automatically fit the contents of the cells.
8. Apply the Grid Table 4 - Accent 1 table style (second column, fourth row in the *Grid Tables* section) and remove the check mark from the *First Column* check box.
9. Click the Border Styles button arrow, click the *Double solid lines, 1/2 pt* option (first column, third row in the *Theme Borders* section), and then draw a border around all four sides of the table.
10. Save the document and name it **7-CostsTable**.
11. Print and then close **7-CostsTable**.

Figure 7.2 Assessment 2

PROPERTY REPLACEMENT COSTS	
Accounts receivable	$95,460
Business personal property	$1,367,340
Legal liability	$75,415
Earnings and expenses	$945,235
Total	

Assessment 3 — Format a Table on Transportation Services

1. Open **ServicesTable** and then save it with the name **7-ServicesTable**.
2. Insert a new column at the left of the table and then merge the cells. Type Metro Area in the merged cell, press the Enter key, and then type Transportation Services.
3. Select the text in the first column, change the font size to 16 points, and then click the Text Direction button two times to rotate the text. ***Hint: The Text Direction button is in the Alignment group on the Table Tools Layout tab.***
4. Center-align (using the Align Center button) the text in the first column.
5. Change the width of the first column to 0.9 inch and the width of the third column to 1.1 inches.
6. Apply the Grid Table 5 Dark - Accent 5 table style (sixth column, fifth row in the *Grid Tables* section).

7. Horizontally center the table on the page.
8. Indent the text in the three cells below the cell containing the text *Valley Railroad,* as shown in Figure 7.3. ***Hint: Use Ctrl + Tab to create the indent in each cell.***
9. Apply italic and bold formatting to the four headings in the second column (*Langley City Transit, Valley Railroad, Mainline Bus,* and *Village Travel Card*).
10. Save, print, and then close **7-ServicesTable**.

Figure 7.3 Assessment 3

Metro Area Transportation Services	Service	Telephone
	Langley City Transit	
	Subway and bus information	(507) 555-3049
	Service status hotline	(507) 555-4123
	Travel information	(507) 555-4993
	Valley Railroad	
	Railway information	(202) 555-2300
	Status hotline	(202) 555-2343
	Travel information	(202) 555-2132
	Mainline Bus	
	Bus routes	(507) 555-6530
	Emergency hotline	(507) 555-6798
	Travel information	(507) 555-7542
	Village Travel Card	
	Village office	(507) 555-1232
	Card inquiries	(507) 555-1930

Assessment 4

Insert Formulas in a Table

1. In this chapter, you learned how to insert formulas in a table. Experiment with writing formulas (consider using the Help feature or another reference) and then open **FinAnalysis**. Save the document and name it **7-FinAnalysis**.
2. Apply the Grid Table 4 - Accent 6 table style (last column, fourth row in the *Grid Tables* section) to the table and then apply other formatting so your table appears similar to the one in Figure 7.4.
3. Insert a formula in cell B13 that sums the amounts in cells B6 through B12. Apply the #,##0 format. Type a dollar symbol ($) before the amount. Complete similar steps to insert formulas and dollar symbols in cells C13, D13, and E13.
4. Insert a formula in cell B14 that subtracts the amount in B13 from the amount in B4. Apply the #,##0 format. ***Hint: The formula should look like this:* =(B4-B13)**. Type a dollar symbol before the amount. Complete similar steps to insert formulas and dollar symbols in cells C14, D14, and E14.
5. Save, print, and then close **7-FinAnalysis**.

Figure 7.4 Assessment 4

TRI-STATE PRODUCTS				
Financial Analysis				
	2018	2019	2020	2021
Revenue	$1,450,348	$1,538,239	$1,634,235	$1,523,455
Expenses				
Facilities	$250,220	$323,780	$312,485	$322,655
Materials	$93,235	$102,390	$87,340	$115,320
Payroll	$354,390	$374,280	$380,120	$365,120
Benefits	$32,340	$35,039	$37,345	$36,545
Marketing	$29,575	$28,350	$30,310	$31,800
Transportation	$4,492	$5,489	$5,129	$6,349
Miscellaneous	$4,075	$3,976	$4,788	$5,120
Total				
Net Revenue				

Visual Benchmark

Activity 1

Create a Cover Letter Containing a Table

1. Click the File tab, click the *New* option, and then double-click the *Single spaced (blank)* template.
2. At the single-spaced blank document, type the letter shown in Figure 7.5. Create and format the table in the letter as shown in the figure. ***Hint: Apply the Grid Table 4 - Accent 1 table style*** (second column, fourth row in the *Grid Tables* section).
3. Save the completed document and name it **7-CoverLtr**.
4. Print and then close **7-CoverLtr**.

Activity 2

Insert and Format a Quick Table

1. At a blank document, insert the Calendar 1 quick table and then format the calendar so it appears as shown in Figure 7.6. (You may want to turn on gridlines to see the cells in the calendar.) Consider the following when formatting the calendar:
   a. Increase the size of the calendar so it is approximately 6.5 inches wide and 8 inches tall.
   b. Change *December* to *October 2021* and then change the font size as shown in the figure for all cells.
   c. Type the dates (1 2, 3, and so on) and the information in cells.
   d. Position the days of the week (M, T, W, and so on) in the cells as shown.
   e. Apply bold formatting and change the font color to Orange, Accent 2, Darker 50% (sixth column, bottom row in the *Theme Colors* section) for all text in the document.
   f. Insert the **FallLeaves** image file from your WL1C7 folder. Change the wrapping to behind text and then size and position the image as shown.
   g. Change the color of the black border lines below each week to Orange, Accent 2, Darker 50% (sixth column, bottom row in the *Theme Colors* section).
   h. Make any other formatting changes so your document looks similar to the document in Figure 7.6.
2. Save the completed document and name it **7-OctCalendar**.
3. Print and then close **7-OctCalendar**.

Figure 7.5 Visual Benchmark 1

10234 Larkspur Drive *(press Enter)*
Cheyenne, WY 82002 *(press Enter)*
July 15, 2021 *(press Enter five times)*

Dr. Theresa Sullivan *(press Enter)*
Rocky Mountain News *(press Enter)*
100 Second Avenue *(press Enter)*
Cheyenne, WY 82001 *(press Enter two times)*

Dear Dr. Sullivan: *(press Enter two times)*

Your advertised opening for a corporate communications staff writer describes interesting challenges. As you can see from the table below, my skills and experience are excellent matches for the position. *(press Enter two times)*

QUALIFICATIONS AND SKILLS	
Your Requirement	**My Experience, Skills, and Value Offered**
Two years of business writing experience	Four years of experience creating diverse business messages, from corporate communications to feature articles and radio broadcast material.
Ability to complete projects on deadline	Proven project coordination skills and tight deadline focus. My current role as producer of a daily three-hour talk-radio program requires planning, coordination, and execution of many detailed tasks, always in the face of inflexible deadlines.
Oral presentation skills	Unusually broad experience, including high-profile roles as an on-air radio presence and "the voice" for an on-hold telephone message company.
Relevant education (BA or BS)	BA in Mass Communications; one year post-graduate study in Multimedia Communications.

As you will note from the enclosed résumé, my experience encompasses corporate, print media, and multimedia environments. I offer a diverse and proven skill set that can help your company create and deliver its message to various audiences to build image, market presence, and revenue. I look forward to meeting with you to discuss the value I can offer your company. *(press Enter two times)*

Sincerely, *(press Enter four times)*

Marcus Tolliver *(press Enter two times)*

Enclosure: Résumé

Figure 7.6 Visual Benchmark 2

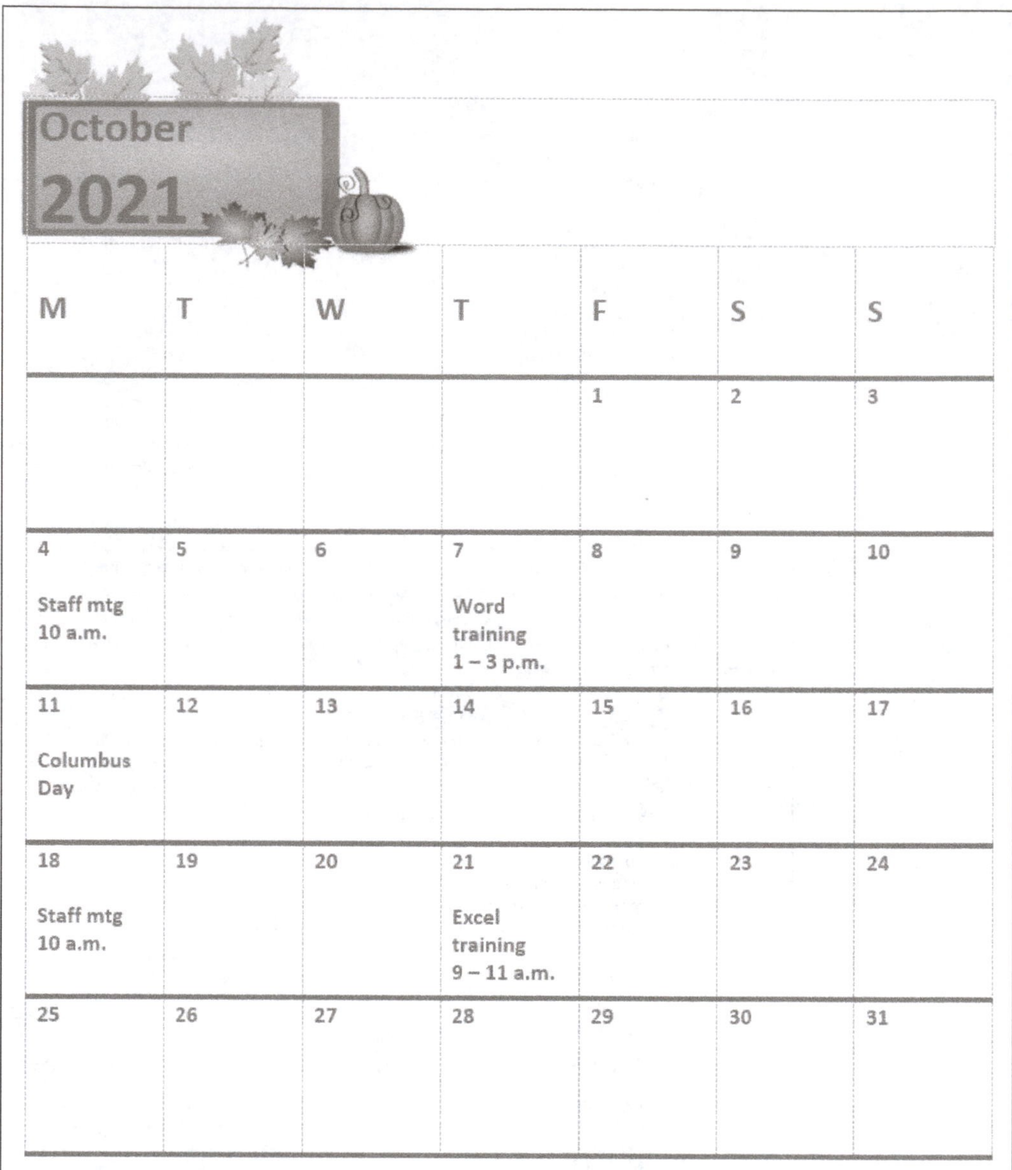

October 2021						
M	T	W	T	F	S	S
				1	2	3
4 Staff mtg 10 a.m.	5	6	7 Word training 1 – 3 p.m.	8	9	10
11 Columbus Day	12	13	14	15	16	17
18 Staff mtg 10 a.m.	19	20	21 Excel training 9 – 11 a.m.	22	23	24
25	26	27	28	29	30	31

Case Study

Part 1

You have recently been hired as an office clerk for a landscaping business, Landmark Landscaping, which has two small offices in your city. The person who held the position before you kept track of monthly sales using Word, and the office manager would prefer that you continue using that application. Open the document **LLMoSales** and then save it with the name **7-LLMoSales**. After reviewing the information, you decide that a table would be a better format for maintaining and presenting the data. Convert the data to a table and modify its appearance so that it is easy to read and understand. Insert a total row at the bottom of the table and then insert formulas to sum the totals in the columns that contain amounts. Apply formatting to the table to enhance its appearance. Determine a color theme for the table and then continue to use that color theme when preparing other documents for Landmark Landscaping. Save, print, and then close the document.

Part 2

The office manager of Landmark Landscaping would like you to create a monthly calendar (use the current month) using a quick table. Insert the dates in the calendar and apply formatting using the color theme you determined for the company in Part 1. Consider inserting an image or any other element to enhance the appearance of the calendar. Add the following information to the calendar:

- Sales meeting on the first Tuesday of the month from 10:00 to 11:30 a.m.
- Product presentation the second Wednesday of the month from 9:00 to 10:00 a.m.
- Sales training the fourth Thursday of the month from 2:00 to 4:30 p.m.

Save the completed calendar and name the document **7-LLCalendar**. Print and then close the document.

Part 3

The office manager has started to produce a training document on how to create and format tables. He has asked you to add information on keyboard shortcuts for selecting and moving within tables. Use the Help feature to learn about the keyboard shortcuts available for editing and moving within tables. (Look specifically for information on selecting text and graphics in a table, moving within a table, and any additional keyboard shortcuts related to tables.) With the information you find, create a table. Format the table to enhance its appearance and apply colors that match the color scheme you chose in Part 1. Save the document and name it **7-Shortcuts**. Print and then close the document.

Part 4

One of the landscape architects at Landmark Landscaping has asked you to prepare a table containing information on the trees that need to be ordered next month. She would also like you to include the Latin names for the trees, because this information is important when ordering. Create a table that contains the common name of each tree, the Latin name, the quantity required, and the price per tree, as shown in Figure 7.7. Use the internet (or any other resource available to you) to find the Latin name of each tree listed in Figure 7.7. Create a column in the table that multiplies the number of trees to be ordered by the price and include this formula for each tree. Create a row at the bottom of the table that calculates the total order (note that totals are not required for the columns with the quantity required and the price per tree). Format and enhance the table so it is attractive and easy to read and apply colors that match the color scheme you chose in Part 1. Save the document and name it **7-LLTrees**. Print and then close the document.

Figure 7.7 Case Study, Part 4

Douglas Fir, 15 required, $1.99 per tree
Elm, 10 required, $2.49 per tree
Western Hemlock, 10 required, $1.89 per tree
Red Maple, 8 required, $6.99 per tree
Ponderosa Pine, 5 required, $2.69 per tree

Applying and Customizing Formatting

The online course includes additional review and assessment resources.

Skills Assessment

Assessment 1

Define and Apply Custom Bullets and Multilevel Lists to a Document

1. Open **TechTimeline** and then save it with the name **8-TechTimeline**.
2. Select the questions below the heading *Technology Information Questions* and then insert check mark (✓) bullets.
3. Define a computer symbol bullet in 14-point font size and then apply the symbol bullet to the 11 paragraphs of text below the heading *Technology Timeline: Personal Communications Technology*. (To find the computer symbol, select the Wingdings font at the Symbol dialog box and then type 58 in the *Character code* text box.)
4. Select the paragraphs of text below the heading *Information Systems and Commerce* (on page 2), click the Multilevel List button, and then click the middle option in the top row of the *List Library* section.
5. Select the paragraphs of text below the heading *Internet* (on page 3) and then apply the same multilevel list formatting.
6. Save and then print page 3 of **8-TechTimeline**.
7. Select the paragraphs of text below the heading *Information Systems and Commerce* and then define a new multilevel list with the following specifications:
   a. Level 1 inserts arabic numbers (1, 2, 3), each followed by a period. The numbers are aligned at the left margin (at 0 inch) and the text indent is 0.25 inch.
   b. Level 2 inserts capital letters (A, B, C), each followed by a period. The letters are aligned 0.25 inch from the left margin and the text indent is 0.5 inch.
   c. Level 3 inserts arabic numbers (1, 2, 3), each followed by a right parenthesis. The numbers are aligned 0.5 inch from the left margin and the text indent is 0.75 inch.
   d. Make sure the new multilevel list formatting is applied to the selected paragraphs.
8. Select the paragraphs of text below the heading *Internet* and then apply the new multilevel list formatting.
9. Save, print, and then close **8-TechTimeline**.

Assessment 2

Format a Health Plan Document with AutoCorrect

1. Open **KLHPlan** and then save it with the name **8-KLHPlan**.
2. Add the following text to AutoCorrect:
   a. Type kl in the *Replace* text box and type Key Life Health Plan in the *With* text box.
   b. Type m in the *Replace* text box and type medical in the *With* text box.
3. With the insertion point positioned at the beginning of the document, type the text shown in Figure 8.1.
4. Move the insertion point to the blank line below the first paragraph of text below the heading *Quality Assessment*. Insert a bullet symbol by typing > and then pressing the Tab key. Type Member rights, press the Enter key, and then type the following lines of text (each should be preceded by the bullet symbol):

   Preventative health care
   Provider quality standards
   Clinical care review

5. If necessary, turn off autoformatting of web addresses. ***Hint: Do this at the AutoCorrect dialog box with the AutoFormat As You Type tab selected.***
6. Move the insertion point to the end of the document and then type the text shown in Figure 8.2. ***Hint: Type** (tm) **to insert the trademark symbol.***
7. Make the following changes to the document:
   a. Apply the Heading 1 style to the title *Key Life Health Plan*.
   b. Apply the Heading 2 style to the heading *How the Plan Works*.
   c. Apply the Frame theme.
8. Save and then print **8-KLHPlan**.
9. Delete the two entries you made at the AutoCorrect dialog box.
10. Turn on the autoformatting of web addresses.
11. Close **8-KLHPlan**.

Figure 8.1 Assessment 2

kl

How the Plan Works

When you enroll in the kl, you and each eligible family member select a plan option. A kl option includes a main m clinic, any affiliated satellite clinics, and designated hospitals. kl provides coverage for emergency m services outside the service area. If the m emergency is not life threatening, call your primary care physician to arrange for care before going to an emergency facility. If you have a life-threatening emergency, go directly to the nearest appropriate facility.

Figure 8.2 Assessment 2

Key Life Health Plan™

https://ppi-edu.net/KeyLife

Assessment 3 Create and Apply Custom Themes to a Company Document

1. At a blank document, create custom theme colors named with your initials that make the following color changes:
   a. Change the Text/Background - Dark 2 color to Orange, Accent 2, Darker 50% (sixth column, last row in the *Theme Colors* section).
   b. Change the Accent 1 color to Green, Accent 6, Darker 50% (tenth column, last row in the *Theme Colors* section).
   c. Change the Accent 4 color to Orange, Accent 2, Darker 50%.
   d. Change the Accent 6 color to Green, Accent 6, Darker 25% (tenth column, fifth row in the *Theme Colors* section).
2. Create custom theme fonts named with your initials that change the heading font to Copperplate Gothic Bold and the body font to Constantia.
3. Click the Effects button and then click the *Riblet* option at the drop-down gallery (last column, third row).
4. Save the custom document theme and name it *WL1C8* followed by your initials. ***Hint: Do this with the* Save Current Theme *option at the Themes button drop-down gallery.***
5. Close the document without saving the changes.
6. Open **DIRevenues** and then save it with the name **8-DIRevenues**.
7. Move the insertion point to the end of the document and then insert the document named **DIGraphic**. ***Hint: Do this with the Object button arrow on the Insert tab.***
8. Apply the WL1C8 (followed by your initials) custom document theme to the document.
9. Save, print, and then close **8-DIRevenues**.
10. Open a blank document.
11. Make a screen capture of the Colors button drop-down gallery by completing the following steps:
    a. Click the Design tab and then click the Colors button. (Make sure your custom theme colors display.)
    b. Press the Print Screen button on your keyboard.
    c. Click in the document, click the Home tab, and then click the Paste button in the Clipboard group. (This inserts the screen capture in your document.)
12. Press Ctrl + End, press the Enter key two times, and then complete steps similar to those in Step 11 to insert a screen capture of the Fonts button drop-down gallery. (Make sure your custom theme fonts display.)
13. Press Ctrl + End, press the Enter key two times, and then complete steps similar to those in Step 11 to insert a screen capture of the Themes button drop-down gallery. (Make sure your custom theme displays.)
14. If necessary, size the three images so they fit on one page.
15. Save the document and name it **8-ScreenImages**.
16. Print and then close **8-ScreenImages**.
17. Open a blank document; delete the custom theme colors, custom theme fonts, and custom document theme you created; and then close the blank document.

Assessment 4

Customize AutoCorrect and Edit a Travel Document

1. Open **TTSAdventures** and then save it with the name **8-TTSAdventures**.
2. In this chapter, you learned how to customize AutoCorrect. Continue exploring AutoCorrect and determine how to turn off automatic bulleted lists, automatic numbered lists, and formatting of ordinals as superscripts. Turn off these three features.
3. Position the insertion point at the beginning of the adventure *European Grand Tour*, type >, and then press the spacebar. (With the bulleted list feature turned off, the text you type should not be converted to an arrow bullet.) Type > and press the spacebar before each of the three remaining adventures.
4. Position the insertion point at the beginning of *Antarctic Exploration*, type 1., and then press the spacebar. (With the numbered list feature turned off, the text you type should not be indented.) Sequentially number the remaining three Antarctic adventures (2., 3., and 4.).
5. Move the insertion point to the end of the document and then type For more information on Antarctic adventures, please visit us at our San Diego office at 9880 43rd Street East or call 619-555-9090. (With the formatting of ordinals as superscripts turned off, the text *rd* in *43rd* will not be formatted as a superscript.)
6. Save, print, and then close **8-TTSAdventures**.
7. At the blank screen, turn on the three features you turned off in Step 2 (automatic bulleted lists, automatic numbered lists, and formatting of ordinals as superscripts).

Visual Benchmark

Create and Format an International Correspondence Document

1. Open **IntlCorres** and then save it with the name **8-IntlCorres**.
2. Apply the following formatting so your document appears similar to the document shown in Figure 8.3:
   - Change the top margin to 1.5 inches and the left and right margins to 1.25 inches.
   - Apply the Heading 1 style to the title and the Heading 2 style to the three headings.
   - Apply the Shaded style set. (You will need to click the More Style Sets button in the Document Formatting group on the Design tab to display this style set.)
   - Change the theme colors to Green.
   - Apply check mark bullets as shown in the figure.
   - Apply symbol bullets as shown in the figure. (The globe bullet is available in the Webdings font, character code 254, at the Symbol dialog box.)
   - Apply automatic numbering as shown in the figure and start numbering with 11 after the heading *CANADIAN CODES AND TERRITORIES*.
   - Apply any other formatting required to make your document similar to the document shown in Figure 8.3.
3. Save, print, and then close **8-IntlCorres**.

Figure 8.3 Visual Benchmark

INTERNATIONAL CORRESPONDENCE

With the increased number of firms conducting business worldwide, international written communication has assumed new importance. Follow these guidelines when corresponding internationally, especially with people for whom English is not the primary language:

- ✓ Use a direct writing style and clear, precise words.
- ✓ Avoid slang, jargon, and idioms.
- ✓ Develop an awareness of cultural differences that may interfere with the communication process.

INTERNATIONAL ADDRESSES

Use the company's letterhead or a business card as a guide for spelling and other information. Include the following when addressing international correspondence:

- Line 1: Addressee's Name, Title
- Line 2: Company Name
- Line 3: Street Address
- Line 4: City and Codes
- Line 5: COUNTRY NAME (capitalized)

CANADIAN CODES AND PROVINCES

1. ON – Ontario
2. QC – Quebec
3. NS – Nova Scotia
4. NB – New Brunswick
5. MB – Manitoba
6. BC – British Columbia
7. PE – Prince Edward Island
8. SK – Saskatchewan
9. AB – Alberta
10. NL – Newfoundland and Labrador

CANADIAN CODES AND TERRITORIES

11. NT – Northwest Territories
12. YT – Yukon
13. NU – Nunavut

Case Study

Part 1

You work in the Human Resources Department of Oceanside Medical Services and your supervisor has asked you to create a custom document theme. Open **OMSOrgChart** and then save it with the name **8-OMSOrgChart**. Open **OMSLtrhd** and look at the colors in the letterhead. Make **8-OMSOrgChart** the active document and then create and then save custom theme colors that match the letterhead. Create and then save custom theme fonts that apply the Arial font to the headings and the Constantia font to the body text. Apply the Glossy effect. Save the custom document theme in the Save Current Theme dialog box and then name it with your initials followed by *OMS*. Save, print, and then close **8-OMSOrgChart**. Close **OMSLtrhd**.

Part 2

Open **OMSHandbook** and then save it with the name **8-OMSHandbook**. Apply the custom document theme you created and saved in Part 1 (named with your initials followed by *OMS*). Apply or insert the following in the document:

- Create an AutoCorrect entry that will replace *OMS* with *Oceanside Medical Services*. Position the insertion point on the blank line below the heading *NEW EMPLOYEE ORIENTATION* (located near the bottom of the first page) and then type the text shown in Figure 8.5.
- Define a new symbol bullet (you determine the symbol) and then apply it to all the currently bulleted paragraphs in the handbook document.
- Select the lines of text on the first page beginning with *Section 1: General Information* through *Compensation Procedures* and then define and apply a new multilevel list number format that applies capital letters followed by periods to the first level and arabic numbers (1, 2, 3) followed by periods to the second level. You determine the indents.
- Insert a cover page of your choosing and insert the appropriate information in the placeholders.

Save, print, and then close **8-OMSHandbook**.

Figure 8.5 Case Study, Part 2

> The OMS New Employee Orientation Program is designed to welcome new employees into the spirit and culture of OMS, to clearly establish health care performance expectations, and to set the stage for success. New personnel are encouraged to begin their jobs with the monthly orientation in order to be introduced to the overall operations of OMS.

Part 3

At a blank document, make a screen capture (use the Print Screen button) of the Colors button drop-down gallery (in the Document Formatting group on the Design tab) and paste it in the document. (Refer to Assessment 3, Step 11.) Make a screen capture of the Fonts button drop-down gallery (in the Document Formatting group on the Design tab) and paste it in the document. Make a screen capture of the Themes button drop-down gallery and paste it in the document. Make sure all the screen capture images are visible and fit on one page. Save the document and name it **8-OMSScreenImages**. Print and then close **8-OMSScreenImages**. Open a blank document and then delete your custom theme colors, custom theme fonts, and custom document theme. Delete the *OMS* AutoCorrect entry and then close the document.

Microsoft®

Word Level 1

Unit 2 Performance Assessment

Before beginning unit work, copy the WL1U2 folder to your storage medium and then make WL1U2 the active folder.

Assessing Proficiency

In this unit, you have learned to format and customize objects to enhance the appearance of documents; manage documents; print envelopes and labels; create documents using templates; create and edit tables; visually represent data in SmartArt graphics and charts; create custom numbering and bullet formatting; and customize a document using AutoCorrect options and custom themes.

Assessment 1 Format a Bioinformatics Document

1. Open **Bioinformatics** and then save it with the name **U2-Bioinformatics**.
2. Move the insertion point to the end of the document and then insert the file named **GenomeMapping**.
3. Press Ctrl + Home to move the insertion point to the beginning of the document and then insert the Motion Quote text box with the following specifications:
   a. Type "Understanding our DNA is similar to understanding a number that is billions of digits long." in the text box.
   b. Select the text in the text box and then change the font size to 12 points.
   c. Change the width of the text box to 2.6 inches.
   d. Position the text box in the middle of the page with square text wrapping.
4. Insert page numbering at the bottom of the page using the Thin Line page numbering option.
5. Save, print, and then close **U2-Bioinformatics**.

Assessment 2 Create a Workshop Flyer

1. Create the flyer shown in Figure U2.1 with the following specifications:
    a. Create the WordArt with the following specifications:
        - Use the option in the fourth column, first row in the WordArt button drop-down gallery (white fill, blue outline, shadow).
        - Increase the width to 6.5 inches and the height to 1 inch.
        - Apply the Deflate text effect transform shape (second column, sixth row in the *Warp* section).
        - Position the WordArt in the top center of the page with square text wrapping.
        - Change the text fill color to Green, Accent 6, Lighter 40% (last column, fourth row in the *Theme Colors* section).
    b. Type the text shown in the figure. Change the font to 22-point Calibri, apply bold formatting, and center-align the text.
    c. Insert the **EiffelTower** image file from your WL1U2 folder. Change the wrapping style to Square and size and position the image as shown in Figure U2.1.
2. Save the document and name it **U2-TravelFlyer**.
3. Print and then close **U2-TravelFlyer**.

Figure U2.1 Assessment 2

Assessment 3 Create a Staff Meeting Announcement

1. Click the File tab, click the *New* option, and then double-click the *Single spaced (blank)* template.
2. Create the announcement shown in Figure U2.2 with the following specifications:
    a. Use the Hexagon shape in the *Basic Shapes* section of the Shapes button drop-down list (ninth column, first row) to create the shape. (You determine the size of the shape.)
    b. Apply the Subtle Effect - Blue, Accent 1 shape style (second column, fourth row in the *Theme Styles* section).
    c. Apply the Divot bevel shape effect (first column, third row in the *Bevel* section).

d. Type the text in the shape as shown in Figure U2.2. Insert the *ñ* as a symbol (in the normal text font, character code 00F1) and insert the clock as a symbol (in the Wingdings font, character code 185). Set the text and clock symbol in larger font sizes.

3. Save the completed document and name it **U2-MeetNotice**.
4. Print and then close **U2-MeetNotice**.

Figure U2.2 Assessment 3

Assessment 4 Create a River Rafting Flyer

1. At a blank document, insert the **River** image file from your WL1U2 folder.
2. Crop off some of the hills and trees at the top of the image.
3. Correct the brightness and contrast to Brightness: +20% Contrast: 0% (Normal) (fourth column, third row in the *Brightness/Contrast* section).
4. Use the Position button to position the image in the top center with square text wrapping and then use the Wrap Text button to wrap the image behind text.
5. Apply the Double Frame, Black picture style to the image.
6. Type the text River Rafting Adventures on the first line; Salmon River, Idaho on the second line; and 1-888-555-3322 on the third line. Change the font for the text to Arial Black and the font size to 22 points and then position the text over the river portion of the image. ***Hint: You will need to press the Enter key to move the text down and then center the text.***
7. Save the document and name it **U2-RaftingFlyer**.
8. Print and then close **U2-RaftingFlyer**.

Assessment 5 Prepare an Envelope

1. At a blank document, prepare an envelope with the text shown in Figure U2.3.
2. Save the envelope document and name it **U2-Env**.
3. Print and then close **U2-Env**.

Figure U2.3 Assessment 5

Mrs. Eileen Hebert
15205 East 42nd Street
Lake Charles, LA 71098

Mr. Earl Robicheaux
1436 North Sheldon Street
Jennings, LA 70542

Assessment 6 Prepare Mailing Labels

1. Prepare mailing labels with the name and address for Mrs. Eileen Hebert, shown in Figure U2.3, using a label vendor and product of your choosing.
2. Save the document and name it **U2-Labels**.
3. Print and then close **U2-Labels**.

Assessment 7 Create and Format a Table with Software Training Information

1. At a blank document, create the table shown in Figure U2.4. Format the table and the text (do not apply a table style) in a manner similar to what is shown in Figure U2.4.
2. Insert a formula in cell B8 that totals the numbers in cells B4 through B7.
3. Insert a formula in cell C8 that totals the numbers in cells C4 through C7.
4. Save the document and name it **U2-TechTraining**.
5. Print and then close **U2-TechTraining**.

Figure U2.4 Assessment 7

TRI-STATE PRODUCTS		
Computer Technology Department Microsoft® Office 365 Training		
Application	**# Enrolled**	**# Completed**
Access 365	20	15
Excel 365	62	56
PowerPoint 365	40	33
Word 365	80	72
Total	202	176

Assessment 8

Edit and Format a Table Containing Training Scores

1. Open **TrainingScores** and then save it with the name **U2-TrainingScores**.
2. Insert formulas that calculate the averages in the appropriate rows and columns. (When writing the formulas, change the *Number format* option to *0*.)
3. Autofit the contents of the table.
4. Apply a table style of your choosing.
5. Apply any other formatting to enhance the appearance of the table.
6. Save, print, and then close **U2-TrainingScores**.

Assessment 

Create an Organizational Chart

1. Use SmartArt to create an organizational chart for the text shown in Figure U2.5 (in the order shown). Change the colors to Colorful Range - Accent Colors 4 to 5 and apply the Metallic Scene SmartArt style.
2. Save the completed document and name it **U2-OrgChart**.
3. Print and then close **U2-OrgChart**.

Figure U2.5 Assessment 9

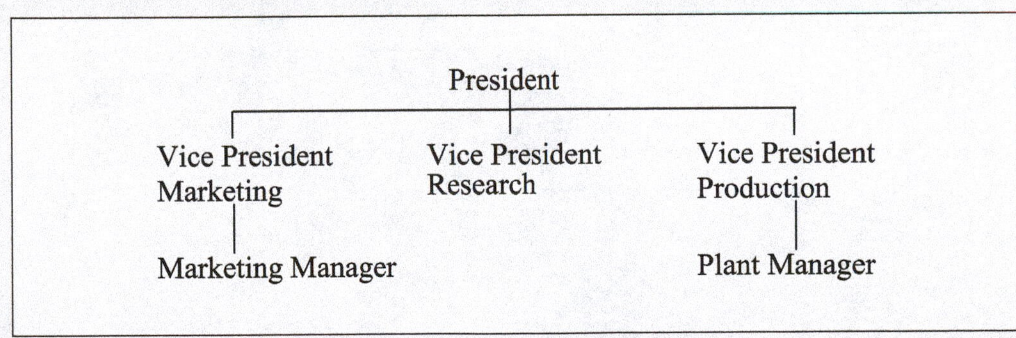

Assessment 10

Create a SmartArt Graphic

1. At a blank document, create the WordArt graphic and SmartArt graphic shown in Figure U2.6 with the following specifications:
   a. Create the WordArt text using the option in the third column, third row of the WordArt button drop-down list. Change the shape height to 1 inch and the shape width to 6 inches and then apply the Square transform text effect (first effect in the *Warp* section). Position the WordArt at the top center of the page with square text wrapping.
   b. Create the SmartArt graphic using the Vertical Picture Accent List graphic. Click the picture icon in the top circle and then insert the **Seagull** image file from your WL1U2 folder. Insert the same image file in the other two circles. Type the text in each rectangle shape as shown in Figure U2.6. Change the colors to Colorful Range - Accent Colors 5 to 6 and apply the Cartoon SmartArt style.
2. Save the document and name it **U2-SPGraphic**.
3. Print and then close **U2-SPGraphic**.

Figure U2.6 Assessment 10

Assessment 11

Format a Stock Awards Document

1. Open **CMStocks** and then save it with the name **U2-CMStocks**.
2. Apply the Title style to the title *Clearline Manufacturing*.
3. Apply the Heading 1 style to the headings *Stock Awards* and *Employee Stock Plan*.
4. Apply the Centered style set.
5. Select the bulleted paragraphs of text and then define and apply a new picture bullet using the **BlueCircle** image file in your WL1U2 folder.
6. Select the lines of text below the heading *Employee Stock Plan* and then apply a multilevel list (middle option in the top row of the *List Library* section of the Multilevel List button drop-down list).
7. With the text still selected, define a new multilevel list that inserts capital letters followed by periods (A., B., C.) for level 2 and arabic numbers followed by periods (1., 2., 3.) for level 3. (Make sure the new multilevel list applies to the selected text.)
8. Save, print, and then close **U2-CMStocks**.

Assessment 12

Format an Equipment Rental Agreement

1. At a blank document, create custom theme colors named with your initials that change the Text/Background - Dark 2 color to Orange, Accent 2, Darker 50% (sixth column, last row in the *Theme Colors* section) and the Accent 1 color to Green, Accent 6, Darker 25% (tenth column, fifth row in the *Theme Colors* section).
2. Create custom theme fonts named with your initials that apply the Verdana font to headings and the Cambria font to body text.
3. Save the custom document theme and name it with your initials. (Do this with the *Save Current Theme* option at the Themes button drop-down gallery).
4. Close the document without saving the changes.
5. Open **MRCForm** and then save it with the name **U2-MRCForm**.
6. Add the following text to AutoCorrect:
   a. Type mrc in the *Replace* text box and type Meridian Rental Company in the *With* text box.
   b. Type erag in the *Replace* text box and type Equipment Rental Agreement in the *With* text box.
7. Move the insertion point to the blank line below the heading *Default* (on the third page) and then type the text shown in Figure U2.7. Use the Numbering feature to number each paragraph with a lowercase letter followed by a right parenthesis. (If the AutoCorrect feature capitalizes the first word after the letter and right parenthesis, use the AutoCorrect options button to return the letter to lowercase.)
8. Apply the Centered style set.
9. Apply your custom document theme to the document.
10. Delete the two entries you made at the AutoCorrect dialog box.
11. Save, print, and then close **U2-MRCForm**.
12. Open a blank document; delete the custom theme colors, custom theme fonts, and custom document theme named with your initials; and then close the document.

Figure U2.7 Assessment 12

Upon the occurrence of default, mrc may, without any further notice, exercise any one or more of the following remedies:

a) terminate this erag as to any or all items of Equipment;
b) cause Lessee to return the Equipment to mrc in the condition set forth in this erag;
c) dispose of the Equipment without affecting the obligations of Lessee as provided by this erag;
d) exercise any other rights accruing to mrc upon a default by Lessee of this erag.

Writing Activities

The following activities give you the opportunity to practice your writing skills and demonstrate your understanding of some of the important Word features you have mastered in this unit. Use correct grammar, appropriate word choices, and clear sentence construction.

Activity 1

Create a Letterhead and Compose a Letter

You are the executive assistant to the owner of Clearline Manufacturing, who has asked you to create a letterhead for the company. Use information of your choosing for the letterhead that includes the company name, address, email address, and telephone number. Include an image in the letterhead. Five possible choices are available in your WL1U2 folder, and each image file name begins with *Manufacture*. Save the completed letterhead document as a template in your WL1U2 folder and name the template **CMLtrhdTemplate**. Close the template document.

Use File Explorer to open a document based on the **CMLtrhdTemplate** template. Write a letter to the president of the board of directors, Mrs. Nancy Logan (you determine her address), that includes the following:

- Explain that the director of the Human Resources Department has created a new employee handbook and that it will be made available to all new employees. Also mention that the attorney for Clearline Manufacturing has reviewed the handbook and approved its content.
- Open **CMHandbook** and then use the headings to summarize the contents of the handbook in a paragraph in the letter. Explain in the letter that a draft of the handbook is enclosed.

Save the completed letter document and name it **U2-CMLetter**. Print and then close **U2-CMLetter**.

Activity 2

Create a Custom Document Theme

Create a custom document theme for formatting Clearline Manufacturing documents that includes the colors and/or fonts you chose for the company letterhead. Open **CMHandbook** and then save it with the name **U2-CMHandbook**. Apply at least the following to the document:

- Apply the custom document theme you created.
- Apply title and/or heading styles to the title and headings in the document.
- Add a cover page of your choosing to the document and insert the appropriate information in the cover page placeholders.
- Any additional formatting that improves the appearance of the document.

Save, print, and then close **U2-CMHandbook**.

Internet Research

Create a Flyer on an Incentive Program

The owner of Terra Travel Services is offering an incentive to motivate travel consultants to increase travel bookings. The incentive is a sales contest with the grand prize of a one-week paid vacation to Cancun, Mexico. The owner has asked you to create a flyer that will be posted on the office bulletin board and that includes information about the incentive program and Cancun. Create this flyer using information about Cancun that you find on the internet. Consider using one (or more) of the Cancun images (**Cancun01**, **Cancun02**, **Cancun03**, and **Cancun04**) in your WL1U2 folder. Include any other information or objects to add visual interest to the flyer. Save the completed flyer and name it **U2-CancunFlyer**. Print and then close the document.

CPSIA information can be obtained
at www.ICGtesting.com
Printed in the USA
LVHW051230070423
743760LV00001B/1

9 780763 887179